✦✦

Wildlife's Ten-Year Cycle

WILDLIFE'S

ˉEN-YEAR CYCLE

Lloyd B. Keith

THE UNIVERSITY OF WISCONSIN PRESS
Madison, 1963

Published by
THE UNIVERSITY OF WISCONSIN PRESS
430 Sterling Court, Madison 6, Wisconsin

Printed in the United States of America by
North Central Publishing Co., St. Paul, Minnesota

Library of Congress Catalog Card Number 62-20066

To the memory of
Professor William Rowan
a distinguished scientist,
my teacher and friend,
this book is affectionately
dedicated

Foreword

In July, 1931, on the shores of the wild Matamek River in Canadian Labrador, a private citizen, one Copley Amory, of Boston, Massachusetts, gathered largely at his expense thirty specialists from various fields and from several countries for a conference on wildlife cycles. His objective was to understand periodic abundance and scarcity of those wild animals that affected the lives of his Indian neighbors in the Labrador wilds. Although little of what was said at the meetings on the Matamek materially affected the Indians, the conference produced the first clarification of cycle issues and served notice that there were scientifically trained men interested in cyclic phenomena in wildlife populations.

Since that conference numerous avenues of investigation have been explored. Theories and hypotheses confound the natural-history literature. Most are untested and as a result unanimity is lacking on many aspects of animal-population cycles. For thirty-odd years these periods of abundance and scarcity have been passed off as resulting from chance alone; lacking sufficient precision or amplitude to be acceptable; being so multifactorial as to defy appraisal; and eventually regarded as phenomena easily reduced to ridicule. Not all attitudes are disparaging or skeptical. There are zealots in the field of biology who see cycles in virtually all tabulations of natural and social interactions. From production of pig iron to tent caterpillars, and from ozone quantity to Nile floods, cycles have been regarded as the skeletons or the souls of numerical data.

Doubtless some of the major differences which arise in discussing cycles result from problems of semantics, but to deny biological cycles because they cannot be characterized as precisely as those in electronics or astrophysics is to be puritanically unrealistic.

The briar-scratched shins of the ardent grouse hunter keep him acutely aware of animal abundance. Even the hunter lacking in formal education knows the periodicity of the bulging hunting coat and the lean years when it is empty.

Had the eccentric adventurer John Hornby, in the summer of 1926, taken seriously the impending cyclic low in grouse and hares, his bones and those of his two companions would not be interred deep in the remote Thelon Sanctuary of northern Canada.

In a broad spectrum of intellectual awareness, Lloyd B. Keith has attempted to record, evaluate, and put into proper perspective the divergent points of view on animal population cycles that have been recorded by the skeptic and the disciple. His role in this academic arena is not one to be envied. Within the allotted time, and the facilities available, no effort was spared to seek out those facts which bear on the subject. The scholarship in the treatment of these data is of a high order. To assume that this work will now assure the unanimity on cyclic phenomena would be naive indeed. I have no doubt, however, that a better basis for appraising cycles will crown this effort.

The Department of Wildlife Management of the University of Wisconsin is happy and proud to have sponsored this project. My feelings are highly enthusiastic, although pleasantly biased.

Madison, Wisconsin   ROBERT A. MCCABE
June 5, 1962

Acknowledgments

This book was written during a year's postdoctoral study in the Department of Wildlife Management at the University of Wisconsin. The Postdoctoral Fellowship which I held was supported in part by the Research Committee of the Graduate School from funds supplied by the Wisconsin Alumni Research Foundation. To both the Committee and the Foundation I should like to express my sincere appreciation.

I am grateful also to the Dominion Bureau of Statistics and the numerous conservation departments and game branches in the United States and Canada which, without exception, were exceedingly co-operative in providing much hitherto unpublished data. William H. Marshall of the University of Minnesota, Maurice Brooks of West Virginia University, and Finnur Gudmundsson of the Museum of Natural History, Reykjavik, Iceland, generously contributed their own unpublished population indices for various species. I have, of course, drawn heavily on the publications of many other workers.

Robert A. McCabe was my immediate supervisor; he and Joseph J. Hickey gave unstintingly of their time and were frequently consulted during preparation of the manuscript. I am indebted to each for a great deal of invaluable assistance.

Other persons who were kind enough to read over the completed work included: C. H. D. Clarke, R. O. Stanfield, and A. B. Stephenson of the Ontario Department of Lands and Forests; Dennis Chitty of the Bureau of Animal Population, Oxford; and Edward S. Deevey of Yale University. While a number of their suggestions have been incorporated into the final draft, any errors that may be present are my own.

Arlene P. Knudsen, Patricia Murrish, and Edith C. Keith typed and proofread copies of the manuscript.

Madison, Wisconsin   L. B. K.
September, 1961

Contents

List of figures and maps

Figures

Figures

Maps

Common and Scientific
Names of Birds and Mammals
Mentioned in Text

Birds

Blackgame	*Lyrurus tetrix*
Capercaillie	*Tetrao urogallus*
Goshawk	*Accipiter gentilis*
Grouse, blue	*Dendragapus obscurus*
Grouse, hazel	*Tetrastes bonasia*
Grouse, pinnated (prairie chicken)	*Tympanuchus* spp.
Grouse, prairie	*Tympanuchus* spp. and *Pedioecetes phasianellus*
Grouse, red	*Lagopus scoticus*
Grouse, ruffed	*Bonasa umbellus*
Grouse, sage	*Centrocercus urophasianus*
Grouse, sharp-tailed (sharp-tails)	*Pedioecetes phasianellus*
Grouse, spruce	*Canachites canadensis*
Grouse, willow	*Lagopus lagopus*
Hawk, rough-legged	*Buteo lagopus*
Hungarian partridge	*Perdix perdix*
Owl, great horned	*Bubo virginianus*
Owl, short-eared	*Asio flammeus*
Owl, snowy	*Nyctea scandiaca*
Pheasant, ring-necked	*Phasianus colchicus*
Ptarmigan, rock	*Lagopus mutus*
Ptarmigan, willow	*Lagopus lagopus*

Mammals

Bison, plains	*Bison bison bison*
Coyote	*Canis latrans*

Deer	*Odocoileus* spp.
Fisher	*Martes pennanti*
Fox, arctic	*Alopex lagopus*
Fox, colored or red	*Vulpes fulva*
Fox, European red	*Vulpes vulpes*
Hare, arctic	*Lepus arcticus*
Hare, European	*Lepus europaeus*
Hare, snow or white	*Lepus timidus*
Hare, snowshoe	*Lepus americanus*
Lemming	*Dicrostonyx* spp. and *Lemmus* spp.
Lynx	*Lynx canadensis*
Lynx, European	*Lynx lynx*
Marten	*Martes americana*
Mink	*Mustela vison*
Moose	*Alces americana*
Mouse, house	*Mus musculus*
Muskrat	*Ondatra zibethicus*
Otter	*Lutra canadensis*
Rabbit, cottontail	*Sylvilagus* spp.
Rabbit, English	*Oryctolagus cuniculus*
Rabbit, jack	*Lepus californicus* and *L. townsendii*
Rat, laboratory	*Rattus norvegicus*
Rat, rice	*Oryzomys palustris*
Weasel	*Mustela* spp.
Wolf, timber	*Canis lupus*

✦✦

Wildlife's Ten-Year Cycle

1

Introduction

The aim of this book is to summarize and collate information on those long-term fluctuations, collectively designated "the ten-year cycle," which are allegedly characteristic of certain northern wildlife populations. It is an attempt to review, systematically and objectively, what is presently known about these fluctuations — their periodicity, regularity, amplitude, and synchrony, their relationship to other population phenomena, and their postulated causes. Much pertinent information is scattered throughout the literature, often in obscure or unavailable publications, while the files of various state and provincial conservation departments and game branches contain an appreciable store of unpublished kill estimates — crude but sometimes valuable population indices. This review has been limited in scope to mammals and birds, a strictly arbitrary decision in no way reflecting upon the nature of population fluctuations among other vertebrates or invertebrate forms.

The bulk of the literature on wildlife cycles deals with three- to four-year and nine- to ten-year fluctuations. The former reputedly occur among lemmings, mice, and other small rodents (Microtinae), the latter among snowshoe hares (*Lepus americanus*) and muskrats (*Ondatra zibethicus*); both periodicities are reported for grouse (Tetraonidae). Similar fluctuations have been noted among predator populations which are more or less dependent on the above-mentioned prey species. Three- to four-year cycles have been chiefly associated with arctic and alpine tundra, and those of nine to ten years with boreal forest.

In recent years the evolution of new and better field techniques for studying animal populations has been accompanied by significant contributions to our understanding of population dy-

3

namics. The ten-year cycle, however, has remained superficially investigated and highly controversial. It is my hope that, by consolidating existing knowledge, this review will provide a useful reference for other workers and focus attention on those areas where research is both needed and likely to be most productive.

The term "cycle" has been employed with varying connotation in reference to animal population fluctuations. *Webster's New International Dictionary* defines a cycle as: "One of the intervals or spaces of time in which one course or round of a certain regularly and continually recurring succession of events or phenomena is completed." Cycles are characterized in this definition by three features: (1) completion of a succession of events, (2) recurrence of such a succession, and (3) regularity of recurrence. The concept of regularity has been largely excluded by a number of biologists. Grange (1949, p. 119) thought of a cycle as "not depend[ing] upon regularity, or upon a constant interval length. It depends upon recurrence in the same order. This point as to the nature of cycles must be fully appreciated, for a cycle can show intervals of 3, 4, 5 or other differing numbers of years and still be a 'regular' cycle." Cole (1954) had much the same opinion and stated: "Since the term 'cycle' has come to signify (at least among biologists and economists) a sequence of events repeating in a definite order but without any necessary implication of strict regularity in time, and since populations obviously cannot continue either to increase or decrease indefinitely; it seems that when we speak of a 'population cycle' we are stating little or nothing beyond the fact that the population does not always remain exactly at a constant size." Rowan (1954) mentioned the regularity of some cycles, but evidently did not feel that this was an essential prerequisite; he, like Grange and Cole, stressed repetition.

While concurring that repetition or recurrence is an integral part of cycles, many, and perhaps most, other biologists have also included or implied regularity in their definitions (Elton, 1924; Siivonen, 1954a; Frank, 1957; etc.). Still, the degree of regularity either has not been specified, or it has been phrased rather vaguely; thus we read of "regular intervals" (Clarke, 1949), "rather regular intervals" (Dymond, 1947), "nearly equal interval[s]" (Lack, 1954a), "comparative regularities" (Errington, 1954), "certain degree of regularity" (Huntington, 1945, p. 454), and so on. Predictability is a direct function of regularity, and hence has been described no more clearly.

Leopold (1933, p. 50) referred to cycles as "periodical oscillations of more or less fixed length and amplitude." He indicated that deviations from mean population levels should in such cases exceed 50 percent. Krumholz *et al.* (1957) in "Glossary of Wildlife Terms" gave the following definition of a population cycle: "Recurrent changes in the size of a population which are of such regularity or periodicity that future highs and lows are predictable." Moran (1954) equated cycle and oscillation, describing the latter as occurring when a divergence of a population from its mean level implies a tendency for the population subsequently to overshoot this mean.

I suspect that a majority of population ecologists today would agree with Davis' (1957) definition of a cycle: "In ecological usage the term 'cycle' refers to a phenomenon that recurs at intervals. These intervals are variable in length, but it is implied that their variability is less than one would expect by chance and that reasonably accurate predictions can be made." The key innovation here, doubtless prompted by Cole's (1951, 1954) random-cycle hypothesis, is that variation in cycle length is smaller than expected in chance or random fluctuations.

Scientific interest in the ten-year cycle developed slowly. Seton (1911, pp. 95–106) and Hewitt (1921, pp. 213–234) graphed Hudson's Bay Company pelt collections, and noted the unusual regularity with which several prominent furbearers had apparently fluctuated. But it was not, I think, until Elton's (1924) paper, "Periodic Fluctuations in the Numbers of Animals: Their Causes and Effects," that these fluctuations gained the attention of biologists at large. The fur trade industry in Canada had, of course, been well aware of the cycle for over a century.

Some of the earliest written accounts of extreme scarcity among North American furbearers and grouse are found in the post journals of the Hudson's Bay Company. In December, 1775, and again in February, 1781, for example, Matthew Cocking reported that partridges and rabbits were scarce at Cumberland House on the Saskatchewan River (Rich and Johnson, 1951, 1952). Elton and Nicholson (1942b) have quoted a journal entry made by Cocking during 1776, which stated: " 'Four or five years ago cats [lynx] were very plentiful here and in the woody parts to the Southward etc., but now the natives say there are scarce any; this is attributed to the scarcity of rabbits, these being the cats' chief food. The scarcity of rabbits was also remarked down to the northward where they used to be plentiful, owing to a supposed dearth among them.' " A paucity of game similarly drew comment from John Thomas who, on November 18, 1783, wrote in the Fort Moose *Journal* (Rich and Johnson, 1954, p. 17): "one of our Men came home from the South Bluff, brought only eight Martins [*sic*], and has neither fish, Rabbits, or any kind of provisions everything (he Says) being very scarce." George Atkinson of Eastmain remarked on January 9, 1785 (Rich and Johnson, 1954, p. 262): "I realy [*sic*] do not know what we should have done for Victuals, as not one partridge has been served out this winter nor Rabbits nor Fish to be got tho have had 12 people out from the 18 October till the 7th December with very poor success indeed. . . ."

The observations of Peter Fidler which appeared in his report to the Hudson's Bay Company in 1820 indicate that a seeming periodicity in years of abundance and scarcity was early recognized by some fur traders (Elton and Nicholson, 1942b):

"There are in some seasons plenty of rabbits, this year in particular, some years very few, and what is rather remarkable, the rabbits are the most numerous when the cats appear. This winter the cats have come in considerable numbers, whereas these several years past there was scarce one to be had. Its flesh is good eating, sweet and tender, and they live principally on rabbits; the cats are only plentiful at certain periods of about every 8 or 10 years, and seldom remain in these southern parts in any number for more than two or three years."

Bernard Ross' letter to Spencer Baird of the Smithsonian Institution, dated November 26, 1859, likewise mentions the apparent periodic nature of furbearer fluctuations (Clarke, 1942):

Might I turn your attention to the remarkable circle of increase and decrease that each decades [*sic*] exhibits. In nearly all the Furbearing animals this is observable, but particularly so in the Martens. The highest years in the decade 1845–55 being the extremes and the lowest 1849, nearly the central one. Migration is the only reason that I can assign for such a fluctuation in their numbers; but if so where do they go to? . . . We never find them dead as we do hares, which are quite as regular in their periods of appearance and disappearance.

By the beginning of the present century, MacFarlane (1905) spoke of periodic fluctuations in red foxes (*Vulpes fulva*), mink (*Mustela vison*), and muskrats, as well as in snowshoe hares, lynxes (*Lynx canadensis*), and martens (*Martes americana*).

Perhaps the first indications of grouse scarcity in North America were the closed seasons for ruffed grouse (*Bonasa umbellus*) in New York State during 1708 (Phillips, 1937), and in the province of Quebec during 1721 (Shepard, 1937). Schorger (1945) stated that a clear-cut notion of periodic fluctuations in grouse did not appear until the latter half of the past century. It is probably not too surprising that sportsmen in the eastern United States and Canada were among the first to publicize these fluctuations. In fact, some of the earliest cycle research was prompted by the alarm of hunters over low grouse populations.

Annual shooting bags from private estates have been used to document European grouse fluctuations since the mid-nineteenth century. Siivonen's (1948) blackgame (*Lyrurus tetrix*) kill data for an estate in southwestern Finland commenced about 1836 and Middleton (1934) gave red grouse (*Lagopus scoticus*) bags for an English estate beginning in 1848. Wilson and Leslie (1911, p. 186) stated that the manuscript records of Bolton Abbey contain reports of "no shooting" as early as 1809 and 1811, which they interpreted as indicating scarcity due to disease among red grouse. Periods of high and low populations of willow grouse (*Lagopus lagopus*) were noted in Norway, and have been summarized by Kloster (1921) starting with the low year of 1869. Compilations of red fox (*Vulpes vulpes*) bounty figures in Norway (Elton, 1942, p. 224), and red fox and lynx (*Lynx lynx*) catches in Finland (Siivonen, 1948) began during the late 1870's.

As we will see later, current knowledge of the ten-year cycle is founded chiefly upon the results of six kinds of studies:

1. Analyses of fur returns and hunting-kill statistics.
2. Summaries of observations and opinions solicited through questionnaires.
3. Compilations of literature references about population levels in times past.
4. Short-term studies attempting primarily to discover immediate causes of mortality.

5. Studies of game species (largely grouse) designed mainly to provide information for management purposes, and whose contribution to cycle knowledge is incidental to this objective.

6. Two intensive long-term (ten years or more) investigations in the United States — involving ruffed grouse and snowshoe hares — expressly undertaken to elucidate the mechanism of the ten-year cycle.

2

Types of indices

Establishment of the existence cycles in animal populations must be based ultimately on objective evaluations of available population indices. It is well, then, to be cognizant of certain biases and sources of error which more or less limit the ability of these indices to portray actual changes in population levels.

Fur Returns

Fur returns are the commonest and frequently the sole indices we have to the fluctuations of many mammals. It is clear that aside from changing population levels per se, such other factors as vacillating prices, unstable socio-economic conditions, and varying trappability of animals may at times influence fur production and marketing.

Hudson's Bay Company (H.B.C.) pelt-collection data have been used extensively to delineate fluctuations of northern fur-bearers, and seem particularly well suited for this purpose. Following union of the Hudson's Bay and North West companies in 1821 (Chittenden, 1954, p. 92) under the former's name, the Hudson's Bay Company had a virtual monopoly over "all the non-Arctic regions of Canada, except for northern Quebec, the Yukon, parts of British Columbia, and the outer zones of the MacKenzie River Basin" (Elton and Nicholson, 1942b). There was no marked change in this situation for nearly 70 years, during which time trade conditions were comparatively stable. Naturally, some discrepancies in annual fur totals arose from delayed shipments and losses in transit.

While fur prices at the London auctions varied considerably from year to year, prices paid to native trappers remained fairly steady. According to Anderson (1928) the Hudson's Bay Company did not attempt to stimulate production of any particular fur, but took the natives' entire catch. Neither did the Company hold furs over for speculative purposes (Innis, 1927, p. 87; Anderson, 1928). Muskrat was the only fur subject to major restrictive trade policies, and these existed chiefly before 1845 (Elton and Nicholson, 1942a; Robinson and Robinson, 1946).

Provincial fur statistics may contain errors not found in Hudson's Bay Company data. The provincial figures are often compendiums of province-wide sales; and interprovincial fur shipments prior to marketing are not infrequent. The chances for mistakes in compilation would also seem to be appreciably greater in provincial data. Moreover, some provinces do not, or did not for a period of years, differentiate between wild and ranch fur; this point is especially significant as regards mink and colored fox. The Dominion Bureau of Statistics first began to keep separate production records during the 1943–44 season (J. H. Dickson, *in litt.*).

Speaking of the effect of price on fur trapping in general, Butler (1950) stated: "the annual crop is not greatly influenced by prices except in the more settled areas [where alternative jobs for trappers are available], or in the case of a disproportionately low price for one particular kind of fur. . . . the greater part of the north country is dependent on the fur crop. Here the policy is to trap whatever animals are available irrespective of price, although greater effort may be exerted for more valuable furs, and less valuable ones may be discarded or utilized by the trapper for his own use." The usual effect of increased prices on fine-fur [fox, lynx, marten, mink, fisher (*Martes pennanti*), and otter (*Lutra canadensis*)] production was discussed by Innis (1927, p. 35). "Prices are, as a rule, at a high level, and the animals are caught in all years. A marked increase in price will affect the supply to a slight extent. Greater efforts may be made to secure a larger number by trapping, and more trappers may concentrate on these furs; but on the whole the increase will not be pronounced, since these furs are the occasion for most of the trapping activity in any case." Edwards and Cowan (1957) believed that, up to about 1950, Innis' view was still acceptable, but thereafter prices, even for fine furs, became so exceptionally low as to create the unprecedented situation in Canada's history wherein many northern trappers abandoned trapping entirely.

The effect of this extreme price decline was especially noticeable in the case of certain long-haired furs. The average value of red fox pelts in Canada fell steadily from about $14 in the 1943–44 season to about $2 in 1948–49; during 1949–58 the average price was $1 with a low of $0.55 in 1955–56 (Dom. Bur. Stat., *in litt.*). Sales of red fox pelts have stayed at a very low level since 1949, despite reports of record fox populations in western Canada in the early 1950's. Coyote (*Canis latrans*) pelt production appears to have been similarly affected.

Two questions which bear importantly on the interpretation of fur returns are: (1) Do fluctuations in fur-return data reflect fluctuations in actual populations? If so, are they of comparable amplitude? (2) What is the relationship between the observed and the true peak years? Most workers agree that fur returns are, on the whole, directly related, though not proportional, to existing population levels. There is likely a definite tendency for a higher percentage of most species to be trapped when populations are high than when they are low; thus, fur returns tend to exaggerate the magnitude of fluctuations. By plotting lynx fur figures on semilogarithmic paper, Butler (1942) detected what he considered an important but temporary exception to this rule. He noted that the apparent rate of population increase was greatest during the first year after a low, and took this as evidence of a higher rate of exploitation — probably due to increased catches of young animals. Peak collections of carnivore pelts are believed to occur at least one year later than the true peak (Austin, 1932, p. 76; Butler, 1942; Elton and Nicholson, 1942b). This is ascribed to the greater trappability of predatory species following the disappearance of their supporting prey populations. Chitty and Chitty (1941) have pointed out that the time of year at which the chief prey species declines and the availability of alternative foods must be taken into consideration, since these factors can affect both the actual peak and that suggested by fur returns.

Bounty payments on predatory furbearers may also be indicative of population fluctuations, but have many of the same biases as beset fur returns. In addition, the suspected practice by bounty hunters of preserving the breeding stock when populations are low may further reduce catches during such periods, thereby increasing the apparent amplitude of fluctuations.

Hunting-Kill Statistics

We have seen that the value of fur returns as population indices is limited primarily, although not entirely, by factors affecting harvest — the harvest itself being reasonably well known through Hudson's Bay Company post records and intraprovincial sales. With state and provincial hunting-kill statistics, on the other hand, one has not only to contend with factors affecting the kill, but also with potentially large discrepancies in the kill estimates. These kill estimates have mostly been based on extrapolations from incomplete returns of kill-report cards, or of post-season questionnaires. Kill estimates derived in this manner are apparently subject to numerous biases, which have been labelled non-response, prestige, memory, etc. (Bellrose, 1947; Sondrini, 1950; Ammann, 1957, p. 161; Thompson *et al.*, 1959; Cronan, 1960), and stem from conscious or unconscious reactions by hunters to queries about the size or composition of their bags. While statistical procedures are being sought to evaluate and eventually to negate these biases, they are still present in the vast majority of kill estimates that are currently obtainable. What is even more disconcerting is that biases of this nature are seemingly not always constant from year to year (Atwood, 1956).

Fiducial limits have not usually accompanied state and provincial kill data. Where they have been calculated, their range at the 95 percent level has been as wide as ± 50 percent of the total estimated kill (Barick and Critcher, 1956); such confidence limits are a function of sample variance and size and do not necessarily take the above-mentioned biases into account.

The relationship between the true hunting kill and the population, like that between the actual fur harvest and the population, is complex. This relationship, though poorly understood, is likely direct, but here again the proportionality is questionable. Population density, sex, and age structure, hunting pressure, hunting regulations, weather, etc., could all theoretically influence the percentage of the population taken.

Recent studies on ruffed grouse (Palmer, 1956; Dorney and Kabat, 1960) and sharp-tailed grouse (*Pedioecetes phasianellus*;

Ammann, 1957, p. 127) have failed to demonstrate a consistent relationship between hunting kill and fall population densities. Dorney and Kabat (1960) were able to show from ruffed grouse band recoveries that hunting exploitation rates were significantly lower on adult males than on juveniles. They believed too that hunting pressure increased sufficiently to stabilize the kill of Wisconsin ruffed grouse during 1950–53 despite three consecutive years of population decline. It is well known to sportsmen that ruffed grouse hunting is easier and more productive later in the season after the leaves have fallen; conversely, sharptails become progressively more difficult to hunt as the season advances and coveys coalesce into large flocks. Here, both hunting regulations and weather can obviously modify the kill.

Yearly game bags from various European estates represent another type of kill data. According to Mackenzie (1952) the bags on British estates were accurately counted; thus the annual kill is not simply an estimate. Mackenzie thought it unlikely that all the shootable surplus was harvested during good years and said that estate owners purposely limited shooting when stocks were low; therefore, the bag during the best and worst years may, in comparison to the population, be lower than usual. He concluded that "bags give a fairly reliable index of numbers as a whole, and as will be seen the fluctuations are so great that even allowing for a considerable error, years of abundance and scarcity are still obvious."

Exports of rock ptarmigan (*Lagopus mutus*) from Greenland (Braestrup, 1941) and Iceland (Gudmundsson, 1958), and capercaillie (*Tetrao urogallus*), blackgame, hazel grouse (*Tetrastes bonasia*), and willow ptarmigan from Finland (Airaksinen, 1946) have also been employed as population indices. Williams (1954) has indicated that these figures make no allowance for home consumption; moreover, an entire season's kill may not be exported in the same year.

Questionnnaires to Observers

Annual questionnaires have been used to gather information on wildlife population fluctuations in Alaska, Canada, and sections of the northern United States. The following are the major North American questionnaires and the dates when first initiated: Hudson's Bay Company Zoological Report, 1925 (Chitty and Elton, 1937); Snowshoe Rabbit Enquiry, 1931 (Elton, 1933); Biological Board of Canada Report, 1931 (Williams, 1954); Royal Ontario Museum of Zoology Questionnaire, 1932 (Snyder, 1935); Canadian Arctic Wildlife Enquiry, 1935 (Chitty and Elton, 1937); and University of Alberta Zoology Department Questionnaire, 1942 (Rowan, 1953). The General Union of Finnish Sportsmen (Finnish Sportsmens' League) inaugurated a questionnaire in 1928 (Siivonen, 1948), and this was continued and enlarged by the Finnish Game Foundation after 1944 (M. O. Helminen, pers. com.). Similar inquiries have been made for short periods in Norway and Denmark (Williams, 1954).

The common practice has been to solicit the opinion of observers as to the status of various species in areas familiar to them. These persons were usually asked to report on whether they believed populations had increased, decreased, or exhibited no change during the past year as compared to the year before. Observers sometimes qualified their remarks, e.g., increased abundant, no change abundant, no change scarce, etc., and frequently included comments on disease outbreaks and other phenomena of biological interest.

It is patent that the reliability of questionnaires depends greatly on the experience, astuteness, and veracity of the observers. These are difficult qualities to appraise in known individuals, to say nothing of a large group with which one has had no personal contact. The technique is unquestionably most effective where marked fluctuations in populations occur. The roadside feeding habits of ruffed and sharp-tailed grouse and the imperfect synchrony between snowshoe hare moults and snow cover greatly increase the conspicuousness of these species, thus facilitating detection of changing population levels. Unless questionnaires are vigorously pursued each year and a concerted effort made to retain the continued interest of observers, there is a definite tendency for the percentage of replies to dwindle. This might, over a period of time, introduce a form of nonresponse bias into the data. Elton (1933) has discussed some of the problems encountered in mapping regional trends from questionnaire reports.

Questionnaire data seem to have been misinterpreted at times.

Figures or tables have been presented showing either the percentage of observers reporting an increase over the preceding year (Rowan, 1954; Hickey, 1954) or the percentage of observers reporting an increase minus the percentage reporting a decrease (Fallis, 1945). Plotting or enumerating such values reveals fluctuations, but because observers are comparing one year's population with that of the year before, apparent ups and downs in population levels may represent only changing *rates* of increase or decrease. Failure to recognize this fact probably accounts for most interpretative errors. For example, if the percentage of observers reporting an increase during five consecutive years is 55, 65, 75, 55, and 45, the apparent peak or turning point occurs in the third year when the percentage of observers reporting an increase is 75. The true population peak, however, occurs in the fourth when the percentage of observers reporting an increase is 55. The rate of population growth diminishes between the third and fourth years, but the population level per se does not start to decline until the percentage reporting an increase is less than the percentage reporting a decrease; i.e., the percentage of observers reporting increase minus the percentage reporting decrease is a negative value. Had the percentage reporting an increase in the fourth year been 50 instead of 55, then population levels in both the third and fourth years would have been similar; had the percentage been 45 instead of 55, then population levels would have dropped in the fourth year, and the third year — the apparent peak — would therefore also have been the true peak. (In the examples just discussed, it was of course assumed that no reports of "no change" were received.)

Williams (1954) utilized three of the North American questionnaires in summarizing tetraonid fluctuations, and commented:

Relying as it does on observers of all standards of ability some of whom have lived for only a short time in the area they are reporting on, and dealing as it must with only general trends in a very complex phenomenon, it is not claimed that the questionnaire method is the ideal one for studying population fluctuations; in fact, in dealing with the Tetraonidae where the difference between the maximum and minimum population densities is very much less marked than is the case with the smaller mammals . . . it leaves much to be desired. Nevertheless, if used with discretion and in conjunction with other methods or with the reports of trained observers of recognized reputation, it is a most valuable tool.

Scientific Censuses and Indices

In a number of instances, generally on limited study areas, objective field techniques have been routinely employed in an effort to procure accurate census or index data for "cyclic" species.

One of the earliest census methods used by wildlife biologists was the strip census or King census (Leopold, 1933, pp. 151–53; Fisher, 1939). It was initially developed to measure ruffed grouse populations, but the basic principle has since been widely applied. The salient points are: (1) an observer determines the number of animals within a strip on either side of specified census lines; (2) the total population in the area is then calculated by extrapolation from densities within the strip. The main assumptions underlying the strip census have been listed by Hayne (1949):

1. That in a population animals vary with regard to distance at which they will flush or be seen upon the approach of an observer.
2. That the various classifications of animals (with regard to flushing distance) are scattered about over the study area in a random fashion, at least relative to the path of the observer.
3. That the average of the flushing distances observed by the investigator is a good estimate of the true average of all flushing distances throughout the population being studied.

Hayne considered the first assumption to be essentially true, but noted in the second assumption possible errors whose direction and magnitude varied between species. He took strong exception to the third assumption, the means by which the width of the strip was determined, and proposed a new method of computation.

Palmer and Eberhardt (1955) conducted a statistical evaluation of the strip-census technique as used for ruffed grouse, and concluded that "analysis of the strip census data has shown that population estimates from this method are subject to large sampling ('chance') errors." These errors led to exceedingly broad confidence limits unless census strips were long or grouse densities high. The authors calculated, for example, that in order to obtain an estimate of the true population whose 95 percent confidence limits did not surpass ± 25 percent of the estimated size, 320 miles of census lines would have to be walked when grouse densities equalled 7 per 100 acres; about 145 miles of census lines would be required when densities were 25 per 100 acres. While census mileages in past studies have seldom, if ever, approached this magnitude, the indicated population trends often have been so persistent and clear-cut that it would be unrealistic to ignore them. The long-term censuses of ruffed grouse in the Cloquet Forest, to be discussed shortly, provide an excellent case in point.

Two techniques that have been frequently employed to index grouse populations in spring are ruffed grouse drumming counts (Grange, 1950, p. 39; Petraborg *et al.*, 1953) and prairie grouse dancing- and booming-ground counts (Gross, 1928; Grange, 1950, p. 37). In an appraisal of the drumming-count technique, Dorney *et al.* (1958) compared drumming counts with known numbers of males present. On two study areas, over periods of two and three years, the average deviation of drumming-count/known-population ratios amounted to only about ± 8 percent from the overall mean ratio. No significant difference was noted in the percentage of cocks drumming each year, notwithstanding the fact that population levels differed considerably. The authors concluded that "the drumming count is a simple and efficient method for obtaining indices of breeding populations of male ruffed grouse." Grange (1950, pp. 37–38) mentioned three weaknesses of dancing- and booming-ground counts: silent birds (most common when populations are low), shifting usage of grounds, and the unknown sex ratio. Repeated counts of displaying cocks are essential, as weather conditions, disturbance by predators, and other factors may affect the number of birds present (Ammann, 1957, p. 152).

A Petersen- or Lincoln-index type of census was used for snowshoe hares in Minnesota by Green and Evans (1940). Ricker (1948) indicated that the validity of this technique rests upon fulfilment of six assumptions: (1) Natural mortality among marked and unmarked individuals is the same. (2) Marked individuals retain their marks. (3) Marked and unmarked individuals are equally vulnerable to recapture. (4) Marked individuals become randomly mixed with unmarked individuals. (5) All marks are recognized and reported. (6) Recruitment is negligible between marking and recapture.

There seems good reason to doubt that the first three assumptions were satisfied in the Minnesota hare study. To begin with, since stress of trapping and handling precipitated some deaths, and since the tendency for this added stress to cause deaths was not constant from year to year (Green *et al.*, 1939), we might question whether the survival rate of trapped-released hares equalled that of untrapped hares. Secondly, it is extremely unlikely that all of the fingerling-type bands used for marking hares would remain in place. These bands have proved unsatisfactory for permanently eartagging other species including the cottontail rabbit (*Sylvilagus* spp.). It is likewise very doubtful that the third assumption was met, because both marking and census recapture depended on live trapping. It is common knowledge among field workers that certain animals tend to be "trap happy" and are repeatedly taken in live traps, while chances of capturing others are much less (Musselman, 1923; Young *et al.*, 1952; Young, 1958). If the opinions above are correct, and assumptions 1, 2, and 3 were not completely fulfiled, errors in resulting population estimates must be expected. Failure of assumptions 1 and 2 would elevate population estimates, but failure of assumption 3 would depress them; the net result of all three is problematical.

Confidence limits describing the expected sampling errors were placed on hare population estimates by Green and Evans (1940). These agree closely with fiducial limits for the Lincoln index shown by Adams (1951) and based on calculations by Clopper and Pearson (1934) for the binomial distribution.

Pellet counts have been conducted by several investigators to index snowshoe hare numbers. MacLulich's (1937) data demonstrated that pellet distribution was not random (significantly different from Poisson distribution at the 95 percent level), and Adams (1959) recorded significantly higher pellet densities in the heavier cover. Using pellet counts, MacLulich (1937) was statistically able to differentiate between "an abundance of hares and a moderate scarcity of hares."

Other Indices

Under this heading are included a variety of semi-quantitative and observational data. As indicated later, these include nesting records, notes from hunting diaries, trapline catches, scattered reports of abundance or scarcity, etc. They are crude indices, but are often valuable when used corroboratively or when population fluctuations are pronounced.

Even this cursory examination of typical population indices has revealed numerous shortcomings. Many of the attendant discrepancies and biases cannot now, and doubtless never will, be completely evaluated. Still, these are the only indices we have, and I feel that they can be of real value to us, despite their innate weaknesses and limitations.

3

Are there ten-year population cycles?

The belief that some mammals and birds manifest ten-year cycles of abundance is by no means universal among biologists. Indeed, this highly contentious subject finds many reputable workers expounding opposite views — a state of affairs which seems primarily attributable to the lack of precise census data, and to the subsequent utilization and interpretation of population indices of varying accuracy.

Before examining relevant population indices for evidence of a ten-year cycle, it is necessary to discuss briefly ways of distinguishing between true cycles (as defined earlier from Davis, 1957) and random-type fluctuations or random "cycles" (Cole, 1954). The term "random-type fluctuation" refers here to all fluctuations whose mean intervals are not significantly greater than those in random series. These may, of course, include some true short-term cycles (Davis, 1957), but since we are presumably dealing with a cycle of greater periodicity, no attempt will be made to delimit the former.

Cole (1951, 1954) sought to differentiate actual cycles from random fluctuations by first defining a "peak" in a population curve as any value immediately subtended by lower values — a "cycle" being the interval between adjacent peaks — and then comparing the mean length and distribution of intervals in random series (Tippett's random numbers) with those reported in biological data. Cole developed formulae which predicted (1) mean intervals in random series of different length, both with and without serial correlation, (2) the distribution of interval lengths in such series, (3) mean intervals when some minor peaks are ignored, and (4) the effect on mean intervals of the number of population levels distinguishable to an observer.

The main objection to Cole's approach is that it does not take into account situations wherein successive values fluctuate randomly around a trend (Butler, 1953). Butler concluded that "Since no other objective definition of a peak can be substituted for Cole's, it appears that the subjective choice of the peaks, providing it is followed by appropriate checks, is still the best method." Moran's (1954) criticism of Cole's method is, I think, fundamentally the same as Butler's; Moran maintained that mean distances between peaks cannot provide any real understanding of the nature of a series, i.e., whether or not there is an oscillatory tendency. Referring to the analysis of the time-series data Moran stated that "the only satisfactory way in which we can find out whether this [oscillation] is happening in practice is to make a serial correlational analysis of the series and see if any of the serial correlations found are significantly negative." The statistical tests used by Moran (1952, 1953) to detect oscillatory trends seem highly complex, at least to a nonmathematician.

Measures employed by both Cole and Butler for analyzing population series will be incorporated here in attempting to identify nonrandom fluctuations that also have an element of predictability (i.e. cycles). I have not the mathematical acumen, nor have most series adequate length, to make use of Moran's technique.

Cole's test for randomness has two distinct advantages, strict objectivity and easy application. However, an important limitation is that confidence limits cannot be computed directly for the predicted (from Cole's formulae) mean intervals in different-length random series. Thus the mean interval or average cycle length in a set of population data may be greater than predicted, but there is no assurance that it is great enough to exceed the accepted limits of chance variation. In order to construct the needed confidence limits, 2,001 two-digit random numbers were initially abstracted in sequence from Fisher and Yates (1948). These I next serially correlated by taking a two-point running sum so as to duplicate the autoregression that probably occurs in biological data; for, as Cole (1951, 1954) suggested, it is unlikely that population levels in one year are completely independent of those during the preceding year. [Moran (1952) has, in fact, found strong serial correlation between adjacent years' bags in each of four species of British grouse.] Mean intervals for series of 20, 33, 50, and 100 serially-correlated random numbers were then determined. The size range of these mean intervals in different-length series is summarized by Table 1. Since the distribution of all intervals or "cycles" follows closely that predicted by Cole's formulae (Table 2), I believe the information in Table 1 offers a reasonably good basis for separating nonrandom from random-type fluctuations. For example, in a series of population estimates covering 20 years, a mean interval of 5.4 years or more would indicate nonrandom fluctuations, the probability of a mean this size occurring in random data due to chance alone being less than 1 in 20.

While amplitude criteria may eventually prove useful in delimiting cycles, the as yet ill-defined relationship between amplitudes of fluctuation in actual populations vs. most indices (see Chapter 2) discourages such an approach at this time.

Because most currently available indices are relatively crude and run only for short periods, and because of limitations already pointed out by Butler (1953) and Moran (1954), one cannot rely solely on Cole's (1951, 1954) method as a means of deciding if data are or are not cyclic. Some subjective decisions therefore appear unavoidable, at least until there is a vast improvement in the quality and quantity of indices.

When investigating population fluctuations, earlier writers (Clarke, 1936; MacLulich, 1937; Cross, 1940; Mackenzie, 1952; Butler, 1953; and others) recognized the importance and utility of considering the size of areas from which indices were drawn. Hickey (1954) scrutinized fluctuations of alleged cyclic species at "continental," "regional," and "local" levels in that order. Under "continental" he included areas embracing a major portion of a species range; by "regional" he meant provinces, states, and large fur districts; "local" implied "[a] small area lending itself to the actual tabulation of census data by one or more persons." The same approach is used in the present work, though population changes on small areas are explored first. The term "peak" will be used in the sense of Cole (1951, 1954) to denote any value immediately bracketed by lesser values; "major peaks" will be selected subjectively.

The various North American locations mentioned in the text are indicated on maps contained in the Appendix.

*Population Fluctuations on Small
Areas in North America*

Population indices from small areas for species reputed to follow a ten-year cycle are limited, especially in North America, and seldom span periods of ten years or longer. For just two prey species, the ruffed grouse and the snowshoe hare, are there sufficient data to permit even a tentative appraisal of population trends. Various types of grouse and hare indices have been graphed in Fig. 1. I arbitrarily plotted only series spanning seven or more years, as there seemed little chance of verifying upward and/or downward swings in populations with series of shorter length. However, a number of the latter will be mentioned in the text.

Ruffed Grouse. — The striking feature about ruffed grouse fluctuations shown in Fig. 1 is the agreement between widely scattered areas. The correlation is not perfect, to be sure, but there is general conformity as to years of high and low populations.

The longest run of census figures has been gathered at the Cloquet Forest Experimental Station, Minnesota, and extends from 1927 to 1956, except for a three-year break during 1937–39. This was obtained by means of a strip census, a technique which, as previously discussed, is subject to considerable sampling error. Some notion of the magnitude of this error in the Cloquet data was given by Marshall (1954). He compared initial population estimates with those made from later census runs (on the same day and within three and four days) over the same ground. In the three instances cited, initial population estimates differed from later estimates by −10, −17, and +27 percent. While these are substantial differences, they are still small in relation to the 100- to 1000-percent differences in population estimates between adjacent lows and highs. There is, I believe, no good reason to doubt that such data reflect major recurrent swings in ruffed grouse population levels. Intervals between consecutive peaks (in this case also major peaks) were eight and nine years.

Seven years of strip-census data from two Michigan study areas in the 1930's suggest that high and low ruffed grouse populations occurred there within one or two years of similar trends in Minnesota (Fig. 1). Numbers of grouse seen per day by a group of Wisconsin deer hunters (Buss and Buss, 1947) peaked in 1941, just one year before the Cloquet peak, and reached a low in 1945, one year before the Cloquet low. Criddle's (1930) nesting records from Manitoba, and Grange's (1936) daily observations from Wisconsin both exhibited major peaks between 1922 and 1924 and, like the Cloquet data, indicate low grouse populations during the latter half of the 1920's.

Additional evidence that periods of high and low populations tend to be relatively synchronous on widely separated small areas is found in other, often shorter, series of indices. Four years of strip censuses on the Munuscong Park study area in Michigan (Fisher, 1939) yielded highest densities in 1932; markedly lower populations ensued in 1933 and 1934, and a moderate increase in 1935 was apparently succeeded by a further decline in 1936. Ruffed grouse numbers in spring and fall on Valcour Island, a predator-controlled experimental area in New York, increased steadily from 1940 to 1943, then declined sharply in 1944 (Crissey and Darrow, 1949). Dorney (1959) presented Lincoln-index estimates for juveniles, and hunter-flush data for all age groups of ruffed grouse during the falls of 1953 to 1957 on his study area in the township of Cedar Rapids, Wisconsin. Both sets of indices showed the population falling to a low in 1954 and rising each year thereafter. Grouse on another area (Otter Creek) 80 miles to the southwest underwent a similar decline, but up to 1957 had not begun to recover. Palmer's (1956) census (strip and drumming-cock) data from two Michigan localities during 1950–55 disclosed that spring populations were highest in 1952 and lowest in 1955 on a hunted area; on an unhunted area, spring population levels were highest in 1953 and lowest in 1955. Prehunting-season densities were greatest on both areas in 1950; they were lowest on the hunted area in 1955, and on the unhunted in 1954. Drumming-cock counts from the Pembina Hills and Turtle Mountains of North Dakota during the springs of 1951–58 were highest in 1953; counts were lowest in 1955 and 1957 respectively on the two areas (Johnson, 1958).

Ruffed grouse indices considered thus far from small areas have pointed to major peaks and/or high populations during 1915–16, 1921–25, 1932–34, 1940–43, and 1950–53; low populations seem to have occurred during 1917–20, 1925–30, 1934–37, 1944–47, and 1954–??. Intervals between the initial dates of adjacent high periods outlined above, and also between the terminal dates of these same periods have ranged from six to eleven years and averaged about nine years.

This generalized picture of long-term fluctuations is not without exceptions, however, the most cogent being population estimates from the Connecticut Hill and Adirondack study areas of the 1930–42 New York Ruffed Grouse Investigation (Bump *et al.*, 1947). Grouse numbers in each instance vacillated irregularly. Populations at Hale Brook Park, the mainland check area for the Valcour Island study (Crissey and Darrow, 1949), remained essentially unchanged from 1940 to 1944. The ruffed grouse "censuses" at Wyanokie, New Jersey, during 1916–34 (Eaton, 1934) indicated an irregular increase to a major peak in 1924, an uninterrupted decline to the low of 1928–29, and an uninterrupted rise to a peak in 1932. The abrupt decline in 1933 was followed by the equally abrupt increase in 1934. A 100-acre relict swamp in extreme southeastern Michigan held five to nine drumming cocks each spring during 1939–57 (weather precluded a satisfactory census in 1950, and none was taken in 1954). The relatively minor fluctuations that occurred there were unlike those in northern parts of the state (Graham and Hunt, 1958). Six years of strip censuses in Yancey County, North Carolina, between 1952 and 1957 revealed a comparatively stable population with densities in the highest year just one and a half times those in the lowest (D. J. Hankia, *in litt.*).

Two facts about the six latter areas should be noted: (1) Five are situated in the southeastern-most corner of ruffed grouse range, and (2) ruffed grouse populations on all six have fluctuated irregularly or only slightly, and have in no case constituted long-term swings diametrically opposed in phase to those depicted in Fig. 1.

Strip-census figures from the mountains of northern Idaho (1946–50 inclusive) signified a ruffed grouse peak in 1948 when densities were almost twice as high as during the lowest year, 1950 (Hungerford, 1951). Referring to conditions since 1950, Hungerford (letter dated April 1, 1960) stated: "I could say generally that we have not had any extreme highs or lows . . . , and it looks as though there is nothing we can call a clear-cut cycle within this population."

Other Gallinaceous Species. — A ten-year periodicity has been claimed for several gallinaceous species other than the ruffed grouse, and some indices exist from small areas.

Most pinnated grouse or prairie chicken (*Tympanuchus* spp.) indices are from the central and southern United States, well south of the generally accepted limits of the ten-year cycle. Numbers of booming males on a four-square-mile Illinois study area (Yeatter, 1943; Shelford and Yeatter, 1955) varied erratically during 1936–53, but this range has apparently been deteriorating through changing land use. Davison's (1940) booming-ground counts on 16 square miles in western Oklahoma show a major peak during 1933 and a low in 1937 or 1938. Counts of booming cocks (1943–51) northwest of Morocco, Indiana, were highest in 1943 and 1951, and lowest in 1945 (Shelford, 1952). Data presented by Hamerstrom and Hamerstrom (1955) for prairie chickens near Plainfield, Wisconsin, were interpreted by the authors as demonstrating fluctuations which paralleled the ten-year cycle; to me the evidence is not so conclusive.

Rowan (1948) used 1937–46 hunting-bag records from a locality north of Moose Jaw, Saskatchewan, to illustrate the ten-year cycle of sharp-tailed grouse. Bags were largest in the period 1939–42. In Michigan during 1945–56, dancing-ground counts indicated that sharptail trends were not all alike on five study areas (Ammann, 1957). Thus while Seney Refuge and Beaver Island populations peaked in 1950, and Fletcher area had a major peak in 1950, the Bullock Ranch and Drummond Island sharptails fluctuated irregularly. It must be remembered, however, that sharp-tailed grouse have mainly become established in these areas since 1940, and that over part of the time spanned by the above-mentioned counts populations were probably still in an expansive stage of colonization. Moreover, hunting and perhaps plant succession may have affected the comparatively small populations on such areas. Subjective estimates of sharp-tailed grouse abundance at Treesbank, Manitoba (Criddle, 1930), gave 1902–4, 1912–13, and 1923 as peak years; lowest years were 1897, 1907, 1918, and 1927.

Ptarmigan, spruce grouse (*Canachites canadensis*), and blue grouse (*Dendragapus obscurus*) indices are entirely lacking or they cover periods too short to be of any trend value.

Rowan (1948, 1950a, 1950b) felt that on the Canadian prairies the introduced Hungarian partridge (*Perdix perdix*) was exhibiting a ten-year cycle comparable to that of native grouse and the snowshoe hare. Bag records from the same Saskatchewan area for which sharptail bags were mentioned earlier suggest that partridge populations were highest during 1940–43. The biggest decline evidently took place in both species between 1943 and 1944. No other Canadian "hun" indices from small areas are known to me. Fall populations of Hungarian partridges at Faville Grove, Wisconsin, declined irregularly during 1934–42 (McCabe and Hawkins, 1946). March censuses of partridges on a four-square-mile study plot near Pullman, Washington, revealed marked but irregular fluctuations over the period 1946–54 (Swanson and Yocom, 1958).

Snowshoe Hare. — Indices to local snowshoe hare populations are less common than those for ruffed grouse. Six series are plotted in Fig. 1, and only seven others were encountered by me. Although not precise, the most reliable set of snowshoe hare census figures are from a five-square-mile study area at Lake Alexander, Minnesota (Green and Evans, 1940; Chitty and Nicholson, 1943). These data show a peak population in 1933, a low in 1938, and another but smaller peak in 1942. Trapline catches of hares near Oba, northern Ontario, peaked in 1934 and 1942, with 1939 being the lowest intervening year (Hess, 1946). Observations in central Bayfield County, Wisconsin, revealed peak abundance in 1942 and a low in 1945 (Buss and Buss, 1947). Snowshoe hare pellet counts on West Virginia's Gaudineer Knob (Brooks, 1955, and *in litt.*) suggest population highs in 1942 and 1951, with lows during 1946–48 and again in 1956–57. Data from Cloquet, Minnesota (Marshall, 1954, and *in. litt.*), indicate lowest populations in 1946 and 1955, with a peak occurring in 1950. After peaking in 1951, hare numbers fell to a low in 1954 at Anzac, Alberta (Keith, pers. files).

Criddle's (1938) estimates of relative population levels at Treesbank, Manitoba, are interesting but largely qualitative. They show a high population in 1922 falling to lowest densities in 1924–25 and thereafter increasing to a peak in 1934, but again falling to a low number by 1936. Using traps, censuses, observations, and scatology, MacLulich (1937) followed snowshoe hare populations on three Ontario areas (Buckshot Lake, Algonquin Park, and Frank's Bay) during 1932–35. Numbers on these sites either were high in 1932 and fell continuously to 1935, or rose slightly to a peak in 1933 and then fell. At Cloquet, Minnesota, spring densities of snowshoe hares over the four-year period, 1935–38, dropped from an estimated 250 per square mile in 1935 to about 19 per square mile in 1937; densities perhaps increased a little in 1938 (Morse, 1939). Valcour Island observations disclosed four years of increase to a 1943 peak, and a sharp drop in 1944 (Crissey and Darrow, 1949). The number of snowshoe hares taken accidentally

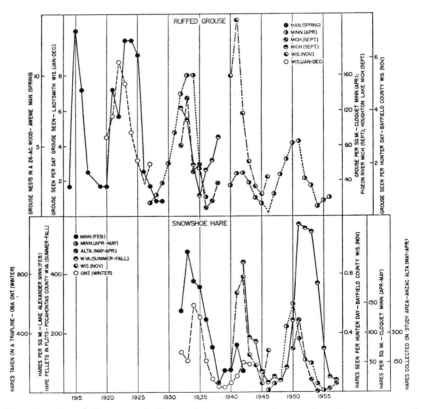

Fig. 1. — Population trends for ruffed grouse and snowshoe hares on small areas. Approximate sizes of grouse study areas: Ladysmith, and Bayfield County — probably about a township; Cloquet, Pigeon River, and Houghton Lake — 4 sq. mi.; Aweme — 23 ac. Approximate sizes of hare study areas: Oba — 89.5 mi. of trapline through parts of five townships; Bayfield County — probably about a township; Lake Alexander, and Anzac — 4–5 sq. mi.; Cloquet — 360 ac.; Pocahontas County — opening below a fire tower. Numerical values of indices and sources of these data are shown in Tables A and B.

during 1951–56 on two experimental traplines in the Chapleau and Gogama forest districts of central Ontario peaked in the winter of 1952–53; there was a very marked decline between the winters of 1953–54 and 1954–55 (DeVos *et al.*, 1959). Hare populations on Bull Island, Montana, dropped about 50 percent from 1953 to 1954 (Adams, 1959). A decline of comparable magnitude evidently took place between the winters of 1951–52 and 1952–53 in a sparse population of snowshoe hares at Sage Hen Creek, California (Hoffmann, 1956).

The indices just outlined denote high or major-peak populations of snowshoe hares on small areas sometime during 1932–35, 1941–43, and 1949–53, while populations were lowest in 1935–40, 1945–48, and 1954–??. Intervals between the initial dates of the adjacent high periods, and similarly between the terminal dates of such periods, varied from 8 to 10 years and averaged about 8.5.

Having reviewed small-area indices of the main North American prey species for which a ten-year population cycle has been adduced, we must now decide whether the observed fluctuations are cyclic, or whether there is adequate information to permit such conclusions.

The Cloquet ruffed grouse census has provided the only series long enough to subject to Cole's criteria. In the 30 years from 1927 to 1956 there were three peaks, the mean interval being 8.5 years. However, there is a gap of three years (1937–39) in these data, during which time another peak could theoretically have occurred and reduced the mean interval to 5.7 years. But 8.5 and 5.7 are both well beyond 4.9 – the approximate 95 percent level of significance for a series of 30 serially-correlated random numbers (Table 3). The probability of having had two peaks during the three-year gap is less than 0.05.

Cole (1951), Butler (1953), Siivonen (1954a), Rowan (1954), and others have pointed out that one cannot expect repeated inter-area synchrony in random fluctuations. Note, then, that with the exception of five localities in the southeast corner of ruffed grouse range, one in the south-central, and one in the southwest, there has been an alignment of ruffed grouse fluctuations on small areas. Population densities have tended to be greatest about every nine years. Unfortunately, we have no knowledge of local conditions in the more northerly sections of this species' range.

It seems to me that local ruffed grouse populations have, in the central part of the range, undergone nonrandom fluctuations of sufficient regularity to be termed cycles. These cycles evidently averaged somewhat less than ten years. There are, I think, insufficient data for definite conclusions regarding the nature of prairie grouse and Hungarian partridge fluctuations on small areas, though highs and lows suggested by indices for prairie chicken in three of four areas, and for sharptails in five of seven areas, line up well with the highs and lows of ruffed grouse populations.

Snowshoe hare population trends in widely separated localities have exhibited excellent agreement. Although existing indices span periods which are far too short for testing by Cole's methods, the obvious conformity in fluctuations and their approximate eight- to nine-year periodicity leaves little doubt in my mind as to their cyclic character. Furthermore, there is every indication (Fig. 1, and in text) that snowshoe hare and ruffed grouse cycles have been broadly concomitant, at least since the early 1920's.

Population Fluctuations
on Small Areas in Europe

Airaksinen (1946) and Siivonen (1948) have reported a ten-year cycle of Tetraonidae in northern Europe. Siivonen (1948) postulated that three short-term fluctuations (three to four years), one having a major peak, constituted a ten-year cycle. The shooting bags from a number of European estates furnish extensive records of local population changes; such indices are without parallel in North America.

Bags of red grouse on four British estates were given by Middleton (1934), and mean intervals of series running for 57, 56, 52, and 28 years were 4.1, 4.5, 4.0, and 3.8 years respectively—all within the range of random-type fluctuations (Table 3). Red grouse kills from four Scottish moors, covering about 80 years (Mackenzie, 1952), similarly imply short-term random-type fluctuations. Statistical analyses of these data by Moran (1952) revealed no evidence of a cyclic oscillation. Annual bags of willow grouse and blackgame on preserves in southwestern Finland (Siivonen, 1948) were just as irregular as in Great Britain, and had mean peak-to-peak intervals of 2.9 to 3.6 years. A subjective appraisal of the above-mentioned records suggests to me that European grouse on small areas have undergone short-term random-type fluctuations, which bear little or no resemblance to the cycles of ruffed grouse and snowshoe hares on small areas in North America.

Similarly, mean intervals in bags of Hungarian partridges on English (Middleton, 1934), Welsh (Matheson, 1953, 1956), and Finnish (Siivonen, 1948) estates and preserves have ranged between 2.6 and 3.7 years. European hare (*Lepus europaeus*) fluctuations as judged from kills on three English estates (Middleton, 1934) and in 22 Danish districts (Andersen, 1957) have also been short-term, mean intervals varying from 2.9 to 4.0 years. Catches of snow hares (*Lepus timidus*) on preserves in southwestern Finland displayed average peak-to-peak intervals of 3.3 to 3.5 years. A possible exception to the irregular short-term fluctuations of European grouse, partridges, and hares is provided by 47 years of snow hare bag records from an estate in Perthshire, Scotland (Middleton, 1934). The mean interval between peaks, 4.9 years, is significantly greater than expected in random series (Table 3); subjectively speaking, one finds major peaks in 1891, 1900, 1910, and 1923–26.

Population Fluctuations within Larger Areas of North America

Population indices for alleged cyclic species are more common at provincial, state, and regional levels than at local levels. Information exists for a variety of prey species and for the chief mammalian predators but the quality of such indices usually leaves much to be desired, and their interpretation demands extreme caution.

Ruffed Grouse. — Kill statistics for the Lake States (Fig. 2) showed fairly clear-cut major peaks in Wisconsin during 1933, 1942, and 1953, and equally obvious peaks in Minnesota during 1942 and 1951. Fluctuations in the Michigan ruffed grouse kill were not so pronounced, but tended to reflect those in the other two states. The significance of the Wisconsin peak in 1956 and the subsequent decline will best be judged after a few more years have passed. One must keep in mind that figures of this sort are subject to many biases and distortions and that probably only the more conspicuous changes in kill have any real significance. In the period 1949–56, Wisconsin's hunter questionnaires indicated high fall populations during 1949–53 and a sharp decrease to lower levels during 1954–56 (Dorney and Kabat, 1960). A similar questionnaire in 1930–35 gave 1931 as the year of highest densities on the upper peninsula of Michigan; numbers were lowest in 1935 (Fisher, 1939).

The ruffed grouse harvest in Manitoba (Fig. 3) displayed major peaks during 1933, 1941, and 1951. Kill estimates for Saskatchewan, Alberta, and British Columbia commenced in 1950; high or peak numbers occurred in these provinces between 1950 and

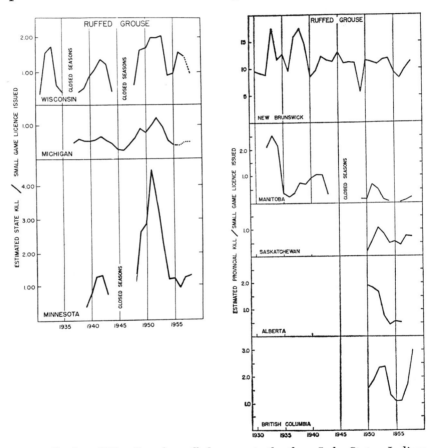

Fig. 2 (left). — Kill indices for ruffed grouse in the three Lake States. Indices computed from data given in Tables C and E.

Fig. 3 (right). — Kill indices for ruffed grouse in five Canadian provinces. Indices computed from data given in Tables D and F.

1953. Questionnaire results published by Clarke (1936), Fallis (1945), and Rowan (1953) indicated the following peak years: Alberta, 1933, 1942, and 1951; Saskatchewan, 1932; Manitoba, 1932; Ontario, 1932 and 1942; Quebec, 1933. A breakdown of the Ontario questionnaire data into four regions disclosed essentially synchronous ruffed grouse fluctuations (Fig. 4). Hunter success on native grouse (combined ruffed, spruce, and sharp-tailed) in Alaska peaked during 1932 and was high in 1942 (Buckley, 1954); success was lowest during 1928, 1938, and 1949. The preceding Canadian and Alaskan indices imply prominent eight- to ten-year population swings resembling those in the Lakes States.

Kill figures for ruffed grouse from five eastern states (Fig. 5) and from one eastern province (Fig. 3, New Brunswick) underwent precipitous, but apparently irregular, fluctuations.

The above provincial, state, and regional indices largely corrob-

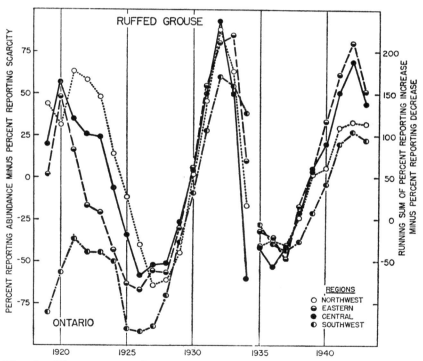

Fig. 4. — Fluctuations in four regional populations of Ontario ruffed grouse, as interpreted from questionnaire data given by Clarke (1936) and Fallis (1945).

orate my earlier conclusions regarding ruffed grouse fluctuations on small areas, i.e., in the southeast they have been much less regular than in the central part of the range where a long-term cycle averaging something less than ten years seems to persist.

Other Gallinaceous Species. — Censuses of Missouri prairie chicken during the springs of 1938 and 1940–44 produced highest counts in 1941 on 2,200 square miles of range (Schwartz, 1945). While kill estimates for prairie grouse (pinnated and sharp-tailed) from the Lake States (Fig. 6) are less complete than for ruffed grouse, they do, on the whole, signify comparable population changes. The middle 1930's, 1940's, and 1950's were seemingly low periods—corresponding to the cyclic lows of ruffed grouse. Manitoba kill data (Fig. 7) exhibited trends largely paralleling those in the Lake States. Peak years in Manitoba were 1932?, 1942, and 1951. Rowan's (1953) Alberta questionnaire designated 1942 and 1952 as peak sharptail years, with 1947 as the intervening low. Kill figures for sharp-tailed grouse from the three westernmost provinces are too limited to be of much use, but generally point to highest and lowest populations in the early and middle 1950's respectively. North Dakota's sharptail kill (Fig. 6) has been irregular since 1947, and provides no indication of a low in the mid-

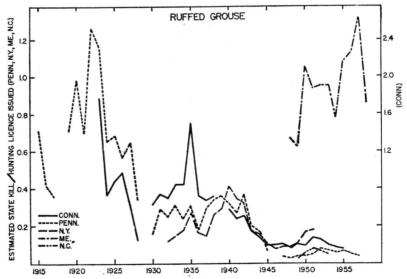

Fig. 5. — Kill indices for ruffed grouse in five eastern states. Indices computed from data given in Tables C and E.

1950's. Nor does there appear to be anything cyclic in the rural–letter-carrier roadside counts of prairie grouse, conducted since 1946 (Miller, 1959).

Hunting success on Alaskan ptarmigan (*Lagopus* spp.) peaked during 1934, and was high in 1925 and 1942 (Buckley, 1954); success was lowest in 1928, 1937, and 1949. Fluctuations in the annual take of spruce grouse in Manitoba were synchronous with ruffed

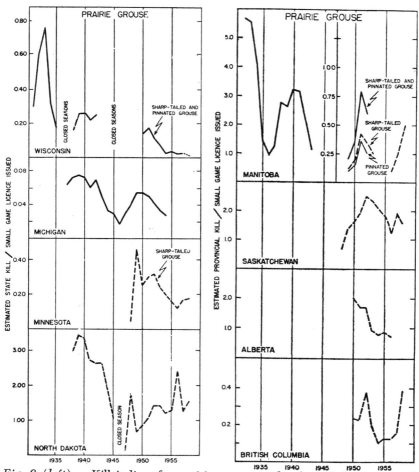

Fig. 6 (left). — Kill indices for prairie grouse in the three Lake States and North Dakota. Indices computed from data given in Tables C and G.

Fig. 7 (right). — Kill indices for prairie grouse in four Canadian provinces. Indices computed from data given in Tables D and H.

and prairie grouse (Fig. 8). The spruce grouse kill in Saskatchewan declined more than 50 percent between 1952 and 1956, following a course similar to sharptails and ruffed grouse (Fig. 9). Peak numbers of blue grouse were shot by British Columbia hunters in 1953 (Fig. 9).

Hoffmann (1956) compiled and plotted literature accounts of relative blue grouse numbers from southeastern Alaska to eastern New Mexico; unfortunately, these data are so scattered and incomplete that any decision as to the nature of past fluctuations seems unjustified.

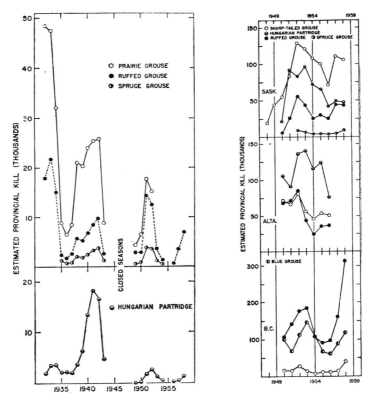

Fig. 8 (left). — Kill estimates for prairie grouse, ruffed grouse, spruce grouse, and Hungarian partridge in Manitoba. Actual data shown in Tables F, H, I and J.

Fig. 9 (right). — Kill estimates for sharp-tailed grouse, ruffed grouse, spruce grouse, and Hungarian partridge in Saskatchewan, Alberta, and British Columbia. Actual data shown in Tables F, H, I and J.

There were major peaks in the Manitoba Hungarian partridge kill during 1934, 1941, and 1952 compared to 1932?–33, 1942, and 1951 for ruffed and prairie grouse (Fig. 8). According to a survey conducted in Alberta, 1942 and 1951 were Hungarian peaks and 1946 marked a low (Rowan 1953). Saskatchewan and Alberta kill estimates for Hungarian partridges and native grouse manifested roughly the same trend, i.e., high during the early 1950's and appreciably lower during the mid-1950's (Fig. 9). Partridge kills were greatest in Wisconsin and Minnesota in the early 1940's and 1950's, and very low during the mid-1940's. A slight decline took place in the mid-1950's in Wisconsin (Wisc. Cons. Dept.), but a drop in 1953 was followed during 1955 and 1956 by the highest kills ever recorded in Minnesota, after which the kill again fell off (Erickson and Burcalow, 1953; A. B. Erickson, *in litt.*). Both the state-wide Hungarian partridge kill estimates as of 1950 and the rural–letter-carrier roadside counts beginning in 1946 have fluctuated haphazardly in North Dakota (Miller, 1959; A. T. Klett, *in litt.*).

Snowshoe Hare. — The best set of snowshoe hare fur returns covers the years 1849–1904 (Fig. 10), and is from Hudson's Bay

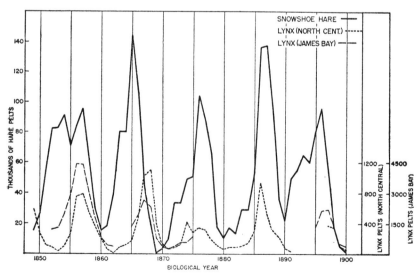

Fig. 10. — Hudson's Bay Company pelt collections for snowshoe hares at posts along Hudson Bay, and for lynx taken in roughly the same region (data from MacLulich, 1957; and Elton and Nicholson, 1942b, respectively).

Company posts on the shores of Hudson Bay. The company did not trade rabbit skins in the interior because their low value did not justify the cost and difficulty of transportation to the coast (Richardson, 1829; MacFarlane, 1905). Mean intervals for pelt collections depicted in Fig. 10 (MacLulich, 1957), and for an earlier version of the same statistics (MacLulich, 1937), are summarized in Table 4. As explained in the footnote of Table 4, differences in the two sets of fur returns involve delayed shipments on three occasions. The true mean interval lies between 4.4 and 5.9 years, and is likely greater than 4.6 years, the 95 percent level of significance in a random series of comparable length (Table 3).

Hickey (1954) noted that peak years selected by MacLulich (1937) in his original consideration of these data were characteristically followed by three consecutive years of decrease. Pursuing this lead further, MacLulich (1957) set about calculating the probability of getting a random series in which: "(a) Population indices for five successive years are successively smaller until the minimum is reached at the fourth year. (b) The fourth-year minimum is less than 0.2 of the maximum known. (c) The frequency interval of occurrence of this pattern varies from 9 to 11 years in the 56-year record . . . ." He found that the chance of a random series meeting conditions (a) and (b) was less than 1 in 50, and that "if a very long [random] series is assumed, the mean interval between recurrences is 59 years. The fact that the rabbit pattern was repeated approximately every ten years instead of every 59 years shows that it bears no resemblance to a rectangular series of random numbers. If only the first condition of three years of decrease to a minimum is considered, the average expected interval is 40 years, which still is not of the same order as the interval for rabbits."

Hunting-kill estimates for snowshoe hares exhibited major peaks in Wisconsin during 1931?, 1941, and 1949, in Michigan during 1939 and 1949, and in Minnesota during 1952 (Fig. 11). The selection of these years was, of course, entirely subjective. Such kill estimates are useful only as very rough approximations of population trends, but trends in Lake States data do seem more significant when contrasted with the extremely erratic fluctuations implied by kill estimates from eastern states (Fig. 12).

The reported Alaskan hare (predominantly snowshoe) kill

peaked during 1926 and 1935, was high in 1942, and was lowest in 1928 and 1938 (Buckley, 1954). A peak hare population that was wholly out of phase with grouse and ptarmigan fluctuations in Alaska, and with grouse and snowshoe hare fluctuations elsewhere, seemingly occurred during 1947.

Results of the Bureau of Animal Population questionnaire — the Snowshoe Rabbit Enquiry — are published for the 17-year period, 1931–47 (Elton, 1933, 1934; Elton and Swynnerton, 1935, 1936; Chitty and Elton, 1937, 1938, 1939, 1940; Chitty and Chitty, 1942; Chitty and Nicholson, 1943; Chitty, 1943, 1946, 1948, 1950). This information was utilized to determine peak and low years for snowshoe hare populations in seven provinces or territories of Canada (Fig. 13). For each year the percentage of areas (1931–37) or observers (1938–47) reporting a decrease was subtracted from the percentage reporting an increase; reports of "no change" were used in calculating percentages but were thereafter ignored. A

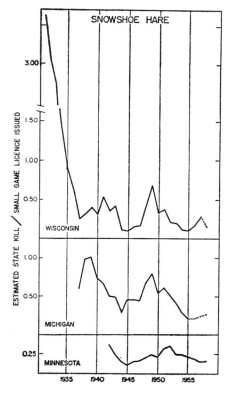

Fig. 11. — Kill indices for snowshoe hares in the three Lake States. Indices computed from data given in Tables C and K.

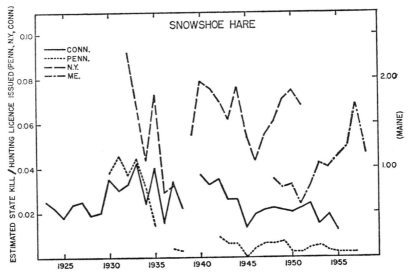

Fig. 12. — Kill indices for snowshoe hares in four eastern states. Indices computed from data given in Tables C and K.

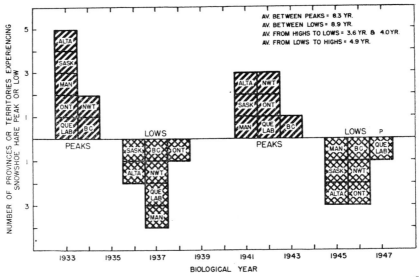

Fig. 13. — Distribution of snowshoe hare peaks and lows in six provinces and the Northwest Territories of Canada, as interpreted from questionnaire data collected by the Snowshoe Rabbit Enquiry (see text for references).

running total of the yearly differences (heeding positive and negative values) was then taken, and all peaks and lows recorded. Although synchronization has not been exact, interprovincial differences in peaks and lows have not exceeded two years. Peak-to-peak intervals averaged 8.3 years.

A similar questionnaire conducted by the University of Alberta (Rowan, 1953) gave 1942 and 1952 as peak years in Alberta with 1946 or 1947 as the intervening low. The precise dates are difficult to secure from Rowan's graph because he does not mention the percentage of observers reporting "no change." MacLulich's (1937) questionnaire indicated that hare peaks in five Ontario regions fell between 1931 and 1933; approximate dates of province-wide peaks were: British Columbia, 1923, 1932; Alberta, 1933; Manitoba and Saskatchewan, 1923, 1933; Ontario, 1923, 1933; Quebec, 1931; the Maritimes, 1931. Table 5 synopsizes peak years given by the above-mentioned three questionnaires.

Observations and comments on snowshoe hare abundance and/or scarcity have been recorded in a variety of scientific and semiscientific publications. Fig. 14 summarizes all such reports, exclusive of those in questionnaires, that I encountered in a fairly extensive survey of the literature. These reports refer mainly to local conditions, i.e., in the vicinity of a trading post, settlement, lake, river, mountain, etc. Hares were considered by me to have been abundant if described as "abundant," "numerous," "plentiful," at "high" or "peak" levels, etc., and to have been scarce if described as "scarce," "very low," "almost extinct," "disappeared," etc. Where two observers obviously were referring to the same locality during the same year, only one circle was plotted. While these indices are among our crudest estimates of population levels, the tendency for reports of abundance to be grouped together and for reports of scarcity to be similarly grouped has been so unmistakable that their nonrandom nature can't be seriously questioned. Groupings tended to center at intervals of seven to twelve years and to coincide in different regions more often than not.

Muskrat. — Following analyses of Hudson's Bay Company pelt collections, Elton and Nicholson (1942a) concluded that since about 1850 (at which time satisfactory records began) muskrats in Canada have undergone "a strongly marked cycle in num-

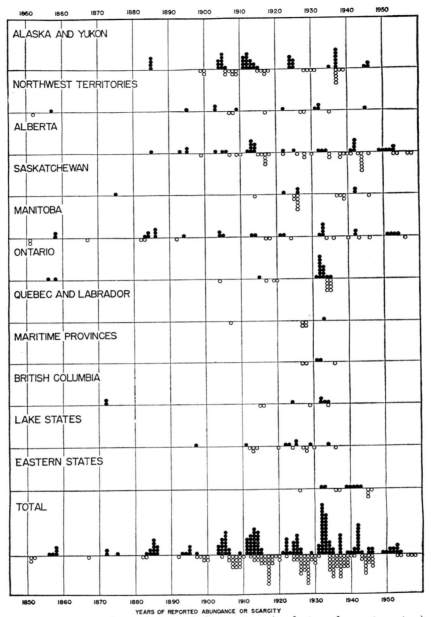

Fig. 14. — Regional distribution of observations (exclusive of questionnaires) on snowshoe hare abundance and scarcity as reported in the literature. These observations primarily refer to local conditions. Solid circles represent single reports of abundance during a single year, and open circles reports of scarcity. References used in compilation of this figure are marked with an asterisk (*) in the reference list (pp. 173–90); in addition to these references, remarks in two letters received by me were used (E. Enquist, *in litt.*; J. D. Waring, *in litt.*) as were three recent observations of my own from Alberta.

bers . . . with an average period of recurrence of about ten years." Cole (1954) cited this conclusion as an example of how long-term cycles may be read into random-type fluctuations by simply ignoring minor peaks. However, a comparison of the mean interval in Mackenzie River District fur records (Elton and Nicholson, 1942a) with that in random series of the same length (Table 6) discloses that the muskrat periodicity is actually significantly greater, viz. 4.9 *vs.* 4.4. Hence, although the fluctuations portrayed by these data are less regular than others we shall encounter, they are, nevertheless, not analogous to a random series.

An examination of the muskrat fur production figures of three provinces — Saskatchewan, Manitoba, and Ontario — revealed that only in Manitoba had mean intervals varied significantly from those in random series (Table 7). Aside from the split peak during the latter half of the 1940's, fluctuations in Manitoba's muskrat harvest have been quite regular (Fig. 15). When the effects of extensive habitat-restoration schemes and regulated trapping

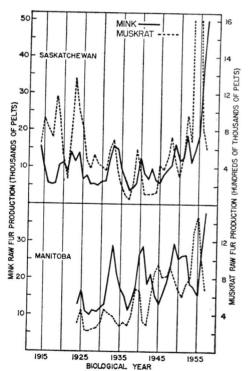

Fig. 15. — Mink and muskrat fur returns from Saskatchewan and Manitoba. Actual data shown in Tables L and M respectively.

on muskrat populations are added to the profound influences of adverse water conditions, snowfall, etc. (the "emergency" factors of Errington) it is, I think, surprising that any semblance of regularity should still prevail.

Butler (1953) had access to fur returns from some 200 Hudson's Bay Company posts in Canada for the year 1916–50. He combined areas served by these posts into 63 sections, and summarized the distribution of peak years within each. The pooled distribution of sectional peaks was then tested by chi-square and shown to be nonrandom, a fact clearly attributable to their grouping at eight- to ten-year intervals. But, since Butler's selection of peaks was entirely subjective, and since the original data were not presented, the most one can say is that the results are highly suggestive. It would have been interesting to have submitted the distribution of all peaks (in the sense of Cole) to such a chi-square test.

Errington (1954, 1957) believed that biologists were unduly preoccupied with numerical fluctuations per se, and felt greater emphasis should be given to other population phenomena in evaluating the cyclic propensities of species. He suggested that drought has had such an omnipotent effect on Iowa muskrat numbers as largely to mask cycles in population levels, and accordingly stressed changes in rates of spring-fall gain, reproduction, behavior, and disease syndromes which apparently concurred in time with grouse and hare fluctuations further north. Errington (1957) stated: " I do not see how these alignments could be due to chance, insofar as there are a half dozen categories of data that have synchronized with each other for known periods of at least 15 to 23 years." Of the factors discussed by Errington as showing possible cyclic influence, reproductive data — particularly yearly variations in litter size — are the most impressive. The significance of variations in adult conception rates and numbers of litters is doubtful, samples being small or differences between years slight. If the criteria used by Errington to detect changes in muskrat behavior and resistance to hemorrhagic disease are valid, his conclusion — that these phenomena are likewise correlated with phases of the northern ten-year cycle — is of extreme interest. Much will depend, of course, on the continuance of these trends in the future.

Lynx. — The fluctuations of the lynx in Canada have long been acclaimed for their exceptional regularity. Hudson's Bay Company records for this species since the mid-eighteenth century were meticulously compiled and summarized by Elton and Nicholson (1942b). Even Cole (1956) has said: "Such painstaking studies as those of Elton and Nicholson . . . give us reasonable confidence that we know in what year a population peak was reached. . . ." The most complete set of regional fur returns is from the six districts of the Company's Northern Department during 1821–91; the longest continuous run is from the Mackenzie River District and covers the period 1821–1934 (Fig. 16). In the total of 426 years of lynx data from the six Northern Department districts, there are only 8 minor peaks and 3 split-major peaks, as compared to 39 major peaks. Mean intervals in Northern Department lynx records (Table 8) varied from 6.3 to 8.9 years, and on this basis obviously cannot be likened to random fluctuations. Moran (1953) analyzed the Mackenzie River District series and concluded that it was oscillatory; commenting further, Moran (1954) stated that "There may be few absolutely certain facts in this subject but one of them is that the lynx cycle cannot be explained as a moving average with positive weights of a series of random numbers."

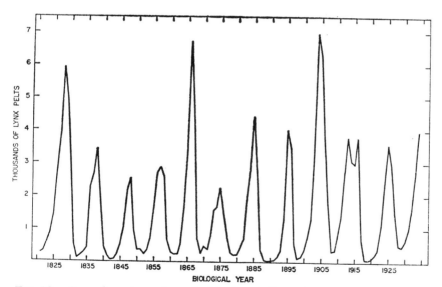

Fig. 16. — Lynx fur returns from the Mackenzie River District of the Hudson's Bay Company Northern Department (data from Elton and Nicholson, 1942b).

The degree of synchronization of major peaks between regions is very striking. During seven cycles the maximum difference between major-peak years in all Northern Department districts was three years. A difference of this magnitude happened but once, the average being 1.6 years. This synchrony extended beyond the confines of the Northern Department to include regions in eastern Canada and west of the Rocky Mountains. As Elton and Nicholson (1942b) comment: "The most extraordinary feature of this cycle is that it operates sufficiently in line over several million square miles of country not to get seriously out of phase in any part of it. . . . There are certainly differences in the peak years, and the whole Canadian peak takes several years to develop and decline. But if the populations were operating quite independently in the various regions, such differences would in a hundred years or less have accumulated to throw them entirely out of phase." Purchases of lynx pelts by the Russian American Company in Alaska during 1842–60 (Buckley, 1954) corroborate Hudson's Bay Company data. These Alaskan fur records contain two peaks — in 1850 and 1858. Moving the peaks back one year to approximate Elton's "year of production," we have 1849 and 1857 as Alaskan lynx peaks *vs.* 1847–49 and 1856–59 as major Canadian lynx peaks in the various Hudson's Bay Company districts.

Butler's (1953) treatment of Hudson's Bay Company lynx figures was the same as described earlier for muskrats, and once again the distribution of peak years since 1916 was proved nonrandom by means of a chi-square test.

Since about 1910, the lynx population in Canada has declined greatly (DeVos and Matel, 1952). Coincident with this decline, there seems to have been a decrease in the regularity of fluctuations shown by fur returns. Recent mean intervals in provincial catches, as reported by the Dominion Bureau of Statistics, have significantly exceeded those in random series in only three of seven provinces (Manitoba, Ontario, and Quebec) and in the Northwest Territories (Table 7). Synchrony between regions has also been less pronounced, major peaks differing by up to four years during two of the past four cycles.

Colored Fox. — Colored fox pelt collections at 21 to 34 Hudson's Bay Company posts in Ontario have been discussed by Cross (1940). Cross found that, between 1916 and 1938, major peaks had occurred during 1916–18, 1926–29, and 1934–38; returns peaked at 81 percent of the posts during 1916–17, at 93 percent during 1926–27, and 63 percent during 1935–36. Intervals between adjacent major peaks at individual posts varied from seven to thirteen years; approximately 94 percent fell within the range eight to eleven years. Cross did stress, and rightly so, the lack of exact synchrony in local population fluctuations, but there was, nonetheless, a manifest grouping of major peaks around certain years.

Hudson's Bay Company fur returns from six regions of Quebec for 1916–48 were graphed by Butler (1951). On the basis of these he concluded that "figures for the central and southern part of the province show a typical nine-year cycle. In the northern sections the data show that until 1930 there was a nine-year cycle in colored fox coexisting with a four-year cycle in white fox. After 1930 the four-year and nine-year cycles exist simultaneously with the four-year gradually dominating the scene." Returns from the two southernmost regions, Lower James Bay and Southern Quebec, exhibited peaks in 1918, 1926, 1936, 1945; and 1917, 1927, 1936, 1944, respectively (back-date one year to get correct biological year). There was but one other (very minor) peak. The greater irregularity of pelt collections in the remaining four regions is evidently a result of their being on, or in juxtaposition to, tundra. Here, as documented earlier by Elton (1942), short-term fluctuations of three to five years are common to both arctic (*Alopex lagopus*) and colored foxes. Numbers of colored fox pelts received at posts lying within the boreal-forest zone may be influenced by fox emigrations from tundra areas and by tundra-based trappers trading to the south (Butler, 1951). Distribution of major red fox peaks during 1916–50 in about 40 sections of Canada was tested by chi-square and shown to be nonrandom (Butler, 1953).

Colored fox fur returns of four western provinces (Fig. 17) describe fluctuations with major peaks in 1916, 1924–26, 1933–35, and 1942–44. Distances between these peaks averaged 9.1 years, amounting to 9 years on eight occasions and 10 years once. Mean intervals between all peaks ranged from 8.5 in Saskatchewan to 4.7 in British Columbia, and were significantly different from those in random series in three of the four provinces (Table 7). The general failure of a major peak to develop in the early 1950's probably reflects the drastically reduced value of fox fur, noted in the previous chapter, rather than a low fox population. In this regard, Rowan (1954) asserted: "During 1951 and 1952 Alberta had a quite incredible population of foxes but the fact will not appear in the fur records, for the simple reason that fox skins are today valueless." Fluctuations in eastern Canada returns are not as smooth as fluctuations in returns from the western provinces (Fig. 18), although they suggest comparable trends. Mean intervals are, by and large, considerably smaller; only in Nova Scotia (Table 7) are they significantly greater than in random series. The

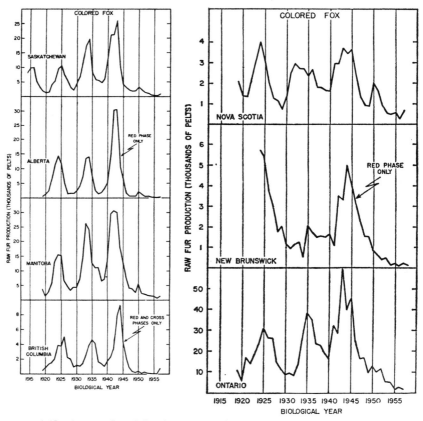

Fig. 17 (left). — Colored fox fur returns from the four westernmost provinces of Canada. Actual data shown in Table O.

Fig. 18 (right). — Colored fox fur returns from three eastern provinces of Canada. Actual data shown in Table O.

increased regularity of western fluctuations was seen also in Butler's (1953) comparison of Prairie Province *vs.* Ontario and Quebec pelt collections of the Hudson's Bay Company.

Coyote. — Hewitt (1921, p. 225), Elton and Nicholson (1942a),
Butler (1953), and others have referred to a ten-year cycle of the
brush wolf or coyote (*Canis latrans*). To my knowledge, however, regional fur returns have not hitherto been graphed and
published. Coyote fur production on the Canadian prairies (Fig.
19), the stronghold of this species, displayed major peaks during
1917, 1925–27, 1934, and 1943. Interprovincial synchronization
has been especially close, the last three sets of major peaks falling
in the same year except for one instance (Manitoba 1927). As was
the case with colored fox, coyote pelts have been practically
worthless since the late 1940's, and hence fur returns thereafter
are a very poor index to populations. The mean interval between
major peaks was 8.6 years, and between all peaks it varied from
a significant 5.0 in Alberta and Manitoba to 4.1 in Saskatchewan
(Table 7).

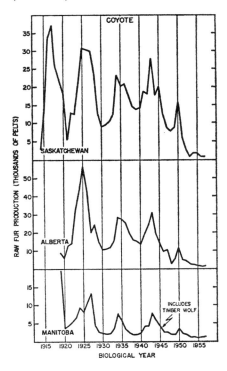

Fig. 19. — Coyote fur returns from
each of the three Prairie Provinces.
Actual data shown in Table P.

Mink. — For just two Canadian provinces — Saskatchewan and Manitoba — was there reasonable assurance that mink fur-production data included only wild-caught individuals. The mink ranching industry has grown steadily over the past 30 years, and today mutation mink alone accounts for around 40 percent of Canada's total mink sales (Dominion Bureau of Statistics). Manitoba figures yielded the smoothest fluctuations, and a subjective appraisal of this limited series points to a fairly clear-cut oscillation of about eight years (Fig. 15). Saskatchewan's returns behaved much more haphazardly, but trends here seem grossly related to those in Manitoba. Neither series had a significant mean interval (Table 7).

Butler's (1953) summary of Hudson's Bay Company pelt collections from 63 sections of Canada produced a significant grouping of major mink peaks at eight- to ten-year intervals during 1916–50.

Fisher and Marten. — The fisher and the marten have been reputed to undergo ten-year population cycles. Cowan (1938) cited early British Columbia fur records giving 1829, 1838, and 1847 as major peaks for fisher. Butler (1953) indicated that the catch of fisher has declined since 1870, but on the basis of major-peak distribution in Hudson's Bay Company statistics, he concluded that this species continues to be cyclic. Trends in the annual take of the top four fisher-producing provinces were dissimilar (Fig. 20). Manitoba's production exhibited an obvious long-term periodicity averaging 9.7 years between major peaks and 5.8 years between all peaks during 1919–57 (Table 7). Mean intervals in the fisher harvest of Quebec, Ontario, and British Columbia did not vary significantly from those in random series (Table 7). There is perhaps still a suggestion of a cycle in the Ontario data; all trace of one vanished from the Quebec returns after 1940, and the British Columbia figures yield a picture of highly irregular fluctuations right from the start.

Elton and Nicholson (1942b) inferred that unpublished Hudson's Bay Company records showed a marten cycle which was less regular than that of the lynx. This is corroborated by Cowan's (1938) graph of marten production in British Columbia from 1827 to 1851. Both the marten and the colored fox trade at Moravian missions in northern Labrador followed mainly a three- to five-year periodicity during 1834–1925 (Elton, 1942). Butler (1953) stated that in recent years low production and closed seasons had made the marten cycle difficult to trace. I could see no evidence of one in provincial fur returns covering the period 1919–57.

Birds of Prey. — Utilizing observational data from a variety of sources, Spiers (1939) concluded that flights of goshawks (*Accipiter gentilis*) and great horned owls (*Bubo virginianus*) into the Toronto region of Ontario had occurred about every ten years from at least 1886. Horned owls usually appeared in greatest numbers a year later than goshawks. These flights seemingly took place one to two years after snowshoe hare peaks in the Hudson Bay watershed.

Quantitative indices for raptors are exceedingly scarce. Fall counts of migrating goshawks at Hawk Mountain, Pennsylvania,

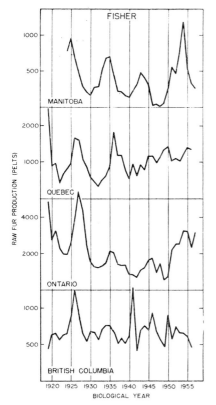

Fig. 20. — Fisher fur returns from four Canadian provinces. Actual data shown in Table Q.

from 1934 to 1948, were highest during 1934–36 with a peak in
1935; comparatively few were recorded in later years, but there
is unfortunately a three-year gap (1943–45) in the data (Broun,
1948, p. 150). Goshawk bounty figures from Pennsylvania show
a major peak in 1936 and possibly another though much lower
one in 1945 (Fig. 21). Bounty payments on horned owls exhibited
a major peak in 1938; no bounties were paid during 1940–43,
but between 1944 and 1958 the yearly kill of horned owls fluctuated erratically. The number of hawks and owls destroyed by the
British Columbia Division of Predator Control (1948 to 1958)
peaked in 1954, although it was equally high in 1948. Indices of
Illinois raptor populations computed from Christmas bird counts
having few goshawk and horned owl observations (Graber and
Golden, 1960) contained no implication of periodic fluctuations.

From the foregoing summary of provincial, state, and regional
indices we can, I think, draw the following conclusions. Kill estimates for ruffed and prairie grouse from the Lake States and
Manitoba are indicative of a relatively synchronous eight- to
eleven-year population cycle. Kill estimates for Alaska grouse and
for spruce grouse in Manitoba exhibit a similar pattern. Comparable statistics from the three westernmost provinces of Canada
span too short a period to warrant definite conclusions. Popula-

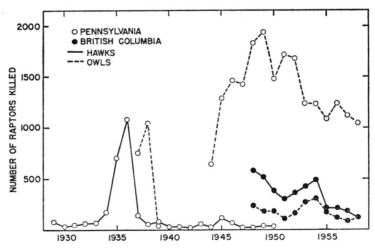

Fig. 21. — Goshawk and horned owl bounty figures from Pennsylvania, and
numbers of hawks and owls destroyed by the British Columbia Division of
Predator Control. Actual data shown in Tables R and S.

tion changes detected through questionnaires point to cyclic fluctuations in Alberta and Ontario ruffed grouse which match those in the Lake States and Manitoba. Questionnaire data are more limited for Saskatchewan, Manitoba, and Quebec but agree well with the concept of a long-term cycle.

Kill estimates of ruffed grouse from the eastern states of Pennsylvania, Connecticut, New York, Maine, and North Carolina, and from the maritime province of New Brunswick have fluctuated irregularly, as have sharp-tailed grouse kill estimates and roadside counts in North Dakota. Hungarian partridge fluctuations in Manitoba and Alberta apparently followed closely the cycle of the native grouse. Minnesota and North Dakota kill figures for partridge show no cyclic tendency, and Wisconsin figures are rather inconclusive.

A 56-year series of snowshoe hare fur returns from the Hudson Bay region is definitely not analogous to a random series, and has major peaks at eight- to eleven-year intervals. Snowshoe hare kill estimates for the Lake States display irregular increases and decreases that roughly parallel the grouse cycle. Kill statistics for eastern states have fluctuated haphazardly. Questionnaires imply a cycle of approximately ten years in provincial hare populations. While peak years have not fallen simultaneously in every province or territory, they have, nonetheless, tended to occur over a vast expanse of central Canada within a year or two of one another. Reports in the literature of snowshoe hare abundance and scarcity are not scattered randomly along a time gradient, but are clearly grouped at seven- to twelve-year intervals and display good interregional agreement.

The mean interval in Mackenzie River District fur returns for muskrats during 1849–1927 was significantly longer than expected in a random series. Manitoba's muskrat production since 1924 has likewise undergone significant long-term fluctuations, while Saskatchewan and Ontario production trends were considerably more erratic. The concentration of major peaks in recent (1916–50) Hudson's Bay Company muskrat data is indicative of an eight- to ten-year oscillation (Butler, 1953). Errington's observations concerning the alignment of certain population phenomena in Iowa muskrats with the ten-year cycle of northern grouse and snowshoe hares must await the test of time.

The ten-year cycle is seen best in Hudson's Bay Company fur returns for lynx during the nineteenth century, being characterized by extraordinary regularity and widespread synchrony. The cycle evidently persists in recent Company records, and is noted also in some provincial fur returns (1919–57). In Canada, south of the tundra, the colored fox manifests an approximate eight- to ten-year cycle which is of greatest regularity in Alberta, Saskatchewan, and Manitoba. Similarly, coyote populations in the Prairie Provinces have exhibited cyclic fluctuations averaging 8.6 years between major peaks. Mink and fisher have experienced cycles of 8.0 and 9.7 years respectively in Manitoba; other provincial fur returns describe less regular population trends, particularly in British Columbia where evidence of a fisher cycle since 1919 is entirely lacking. Major peaks in regional Hudson's Bay Company data during 1916–50 strongly suggest a fisher cycle with a periodicity of around ten years. There is nothing in recent provincial fur statistics to indicate a ten-year cycle in the marten catch.

Raptor indices are too few either to confirm or to refute an alleged ten-year fluctuation in numbers of goshawks and horned owls.

Population Fluctautions within Larger Areas of Europe

I have perused the following European tetraonid indices: red grouse, rock ptarmigan, blackgame, and capercaillie in Britain (Leopold and Ball, 1931; Mackenzie, 1952); willow ptarmigan, hazel grouse, blackgame, and capercaillie in Finland (Airaksinen, 1946, Siivonen, 1952); willow ptarmigan in Norway (Williams, 1954 – after Ruden, 1927–40); and blackgame in Denmark (Williams, 1954 – after Westerskov, 1943). Partridge and European hare indices from southwestern Finland (Siivonen, 1956) and Denmark (Andersen, 1957) were also examined, as were indices for red fox in southern Norway (Elton, 1942, p. 224) and the province of Oulu in Finland, as well as for lynx in the whole of Finland and in the provinces of Mikkeli and Viipuri (Siivonen, 1948).

These and other European indices reflect the same type of short-term fluctuations encountered earlier when considering population trends on small areas. To my mind they are entirely different from the ten-year cycle of North America, and I can see no good reason to accept Siivonen's (1948) proposal that the ten-year cycle is simply the outcome of three short-term fluctuations. Moran (1952) has, of course, analyzed Mackenzie's (1952) British grouse records and found them to be nonoscillatory; Andersen (1957) came to the same conclusion with regard to Danish hare fluctuations, attributing them to random variations in climatic factors. In discussing the short-term fluctuations of European tetraonids, Siivonen (1957) recently conceded that "the fluctuation observed, both as regards birds and mammals and even the spring climate, can be considered to show ± regularity, although it comes very near to a ± random interpretation."

Population Fluctuations within Various Regions of Greenland, Iceland, and the Soviet Union

Population trends in these three countries are treated under a single heading, not because of any known or suspected interrelationship, but because they do seem to differ from those already mentioned for both North America and Europe.

Braestrup (1941) summarized information on rock ptarmigan numbers in North and South Greenland between 1882 and 1939. He classified observations and remarks on population levels into five categories and arbitrarily assigned each a value of from 0 to 4. Yearly mean values based on weighted individual reports were then computed and plotted. Interpreting the resulting graphs, Braestrup said: "It is possible that the numbers of these birds [ptarmigan] (and of hares) in Greenland fluctuate according to a period of about ten years, . . . though the average is somewhat longer during the period investigated." Mean intervals in these crude indices are no longer than expected in random series, but the apparent spacing of major low periods in South Greenland at approximate ten-year intervals is certainly worthy of note.

Numbers of rock ptarmigan exported annually from Iceland during 1864–1939 were used by Gudmundsson (1958) as an index to population fluctuations. While such data have some very obvious limitations, Gudmundsson felt that in many respects they provided a reliable picture of year-to-year population changes. On the basis of these export figures, Gudmundsson concluded that a ten-year cycle had occurred in Iceland ptarmigan until the turn of the century, was lost in a long period of abundance between 1902 and 1919, and reappeared following the crash of 1920. If one ignores the period 1903–19, it does indeed look as though ptarmigan fluctuations have exhibited a ten-year periodicity. Further evidence of a distinct ten-year cycle is found in the 1943–59 trading records of the Husavik Cooperative Store, which draws ptarmigan from an area of roughly 1,500 square miles (Gudmundsson, 1958, and *in litt.*). The number of ptarmigan handled by this store rose continuously from about 4,000 in 1943 to about 22,500 in 1945, and dropped continuously to 0 in 1948 and 1949. Between 1949 and 1954 the trade of ptarmigan increased steadily from 0 to about 21,300, then fell to about 5,300 in 1954, rose very slightly to 5,400 in 1955, and fell to 0 during 1958 and 1959. We thus have two well-marked peaks (1945 and 1954), and two equally well-marked low periods (1948–49 and 1958–59).

Formozov (1942) mentioned that every eight to eleven years (usually nine) yields of white hares (*Lepus timidus*) were good in the European North of Russia, and that in the central zone yields were good every four to nine years (usually seven). Kiris (1953) stated: "Peak numbers of white hares are observed after two or three years of mass multiplication when conditions for the survival of the young are favourable. Afterwards, . . . the hare population declines over a period of two to four years." He indicated, in addition, that long periods of depressed numbers characterize hare populations and dismissed the idea of rhythmicity. Kiris presented a graph depicting hare populations in Archangel Province during the years 1936–51; numbers were highest in 1936, fell sharply to a 1941 low, and except for a minor decrease in 1947 increased steadily up to 1951. White hare production in the Kharovsk District of Vologodsk Province rose from 1935 to a peak in 1938, declined to its lowest point in 1942, and remained very low until the record ends in 1950 (Daniloff, 1953).

Population Fluctuations at the
Continental Level in North America

Grouse and Snowshoe Hares. — Information on fluctuations in continental grouse and snowshoe hare populations comes from annual questionnaires and compilations of scattered observational data. *The Canada Yearbook* (Dom. Bur. Stat.) records the number of rabbits pelted yearly, but due to the extremely intermittent demand in Canada for rabbit skins, such figures are for our purposes practically worthless.

Questionnaires by Oxford's Bureau of Animal Population and the Hudson's Bay Company point to conspicuous and nearly synchronous seven- to ten-year fluctuations in continental populations of snowshoe hares, ruffed grouse, and ptarmigan (Table 9). With the exception of one very minor peak in ptarmigan during 1928, these questionnaires indicated uninterrupted increases and decreases to the designated peaks and lows.

Williams (1954) subdivided North America's grouse range by means of a 300-mile-square grid, and summarized the reported peak years or final years of abundance for ruffed grouse, ptarmigan, and other grouse (sharp-tailed, pinnated, spruce, and blue grouse) within each 90,000-square-mile block. I have utilized Williams' results plus an additional 35 observations to draw up Fig. 22. There seems little question that an eight- to ten-year grouping of peaks or last years of abundance, and marked interspecific synchrony have featured continental grouse fluctuations.

When 300 reports of snowshoe hare abundance and scarcity

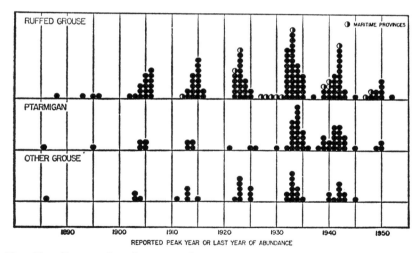

Fig. 22. — Reported peak years or last years of abundance in North American grouse populations (see text for explanation). Data taken mostly from Williams (1954) but also supplemented by information in 18 other references in the reference list (pp. 173–90) marked by a dagger (†).

from all over North America were pooled (see bottom section of Fig. 14), a picture comparable to that described above for grouse emerges. Reports of abundance tend to be clustered with seven- to twelve-year intervals between modal years, and reports of scarcity describe a similar pattern. Though displaying some regional differences in chronology, snowshoe hare peaks and lows have been sufficiently synchronized throughout North America so as not to produce a random distribution along a time axis when scattered observations are lumped.

Furbearers. — Hudson's Bay Company and Dominion Bureau of Statistics fur records offer a Canada-wide index to fluctuations of many furbearers. Muskrat pelt collections from the Northern Department of Hudson's Bay Company, an area which embraced what is now the eastern Yukon, the southwestern Northwest Territories, the Prairie Provinces, and western Ontario, have been summarized by Elton and Nicholson (1942a). The mean interval of this 71-year series (1821–91) for which Elton and Nicholson subjectively deduced a ten-year cycle is a significant 4.6 years (Table 6). Canada's total muskrat production since 1919 (Fig. 23) was more irregular, having a mean interval of just 3.9 years and offering little semblance of a cycle (Table 10).

The longest continuous series of lynx fur returns is that given by Poland (1892), representing the total of Hudson's Bay Company annual sales between 1753 and 1891. This period included an era of great expansion and generally unsettled conditions preceding the 1821 union of the North West and Hudson's Bay companies (Elton and Nicholson, 1942b). Despite these circumstances, a subjective appraisal of lynx returns up to the year of production, 1820 (Poland's 1821), suggests a major periodicity of around ten years, and the mean interval of 4.8 is significantly larger than expected by chance. Fluctuations after 1820 were much more regular, and for the series as a whole the mean interval is 5.8 years (Table 8). Hewitt's (1921, p. 217) graph of Hudson's Bay Company lynx data (corrected by Elton and Nicholson, 1942b) runs from 1821 to 1911 (outfit years), and describes an unmistakable eight- to eleven-year oscillation; thus the mean interval here is 7.5 years. The most regular of all lynx fluctuations are shown in Northern Department totals for the years 1821–91 (Elton and Nicholson, 1942b). During this 71-year period there were no minor peaks, and the mean interval was 9.3 years (Table 8). The lynx catch in Canada during 1919–57 (Dom. Bur. Stat.) exhibited a smooth long-term fluctuation of nine to ten years until 1949. Between 1949 and the peak of 1954 there were two lesser peaks (Fig. 23) which reduced the overall mean interval of the series to a

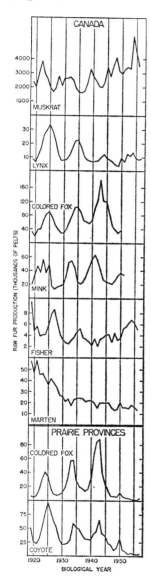

Fig. 23. — Canadian fur returns for some alleged cyclic species. Canada-wide muskrat, lynx, and fisher data, and Prairie Province colored fox and coyote data shown in Tables M, N, Q, O and P respectively. Canada-wide colored fox and mink data from Butler (1953); marten returns from the Dominion Bureau of Statistics.

still significant 5.8 years (Table 10). However, special quotas and closed seasons on lynx trapping have been in effect periodically since 1946 in Manitoba and Saskatchewan, and since 1951 in Ontario. These vacillating restrictions may well have affected the regularity of the Dominion's catch curve.

Hewitt (1921, p. 221) plotted Hudson's Bay Company fox data from 1850 to 1914. Reading as best one can from these graphs, I combined the figures for red, cross, and black fox in order to get total colored fox production. This set of fur returns exhibited major peaks at nine- to ten-year intervals, viz. in 1859, 1868, 1878, 1888, 1897, and 1907 [to obtain the correct year of production one should probably back-date two years, as did Elton and Nicholson (1942b) with Hewitt's lynx records]. The mean interval of 4.6 years between all peaks is significantly greater than expected in a random series. Butler (1953) graphed Canada's total colored fox catch for 1919–50 (years of production), and these data have been reproduced in Fig. 23. There are only three peaks in this series — 1925, 1935, and 1943. The pooling of colored-fox production figures that were used earlier to illustrate fluctuations within each of the Prairie Provinces results in the same type of smooth long-term oscillations (Fig. 23). Coyote fur returns from the Prairie Provinces, accounting for over 95 percent of the Canadian total, depict analogous population swings.

Except for the tripartite peak of the 1920's, stemming from an early peak in Manitoba and a late peak in Ontario (Butler, 1953), Canadian wild mink production during 1919–51 underwent regular eight- to ten-year fluctuations (Fig. 23). Trends in fisher pelt collections have been more uneven, though the suggestion of a major periodicity of roughly ten years still persists. The mean intervals of 5.8 and 5.5 years respectively for mink and fisher are well beyond the 95 percent level of significance (Table 10). Subjectively speaking, numbers of mink and fisher traded to the Hudson's Bay Company from 1845 to 1914 were alternately high and low about once per decade (Hewitt, 1921, pp. 224, 231). Overall increases and decreases, however, were often irregular, and consequently mean intervals are less than the 4.6 years required for significance in a 70-year series.

Marten fur returns between 1835 and 1914 (Hewitt, 1921, p. 224) imply long-term population swings of around ten years duration, especially during 1835–80 when clear-cut major peaks oc-curred in 1837, 1846–47, 1856, 1866, and 1875. The entire series' mean interval of 4.7 years is greater than expected by chance in random data. Dominion Bureau of Statistics figures since 1919 show no cyclic tendency in the marten catch (Fig. 23).

Conclusions that I have made regarding fluctuations by various species or populations must of necessity be considered largely tentative. With a few notable exceptions, such as the Hudson's Bay Company fur returns, available population indices for alleged cyclic species rarely exceed 30–40 years; and as emphasized ear-lier, the quality or trend value of these is often difficult if not im-possible to appraise. Frequently, of course, population series span much shorter periods and their usefulness is further reduced. My remarks as to the reality of "ten-year cycles" are based solely on indices mentioned in the preceding discussion, and may be summed up as follows:

1. Local populations of ruffed grouse in the central portion of this species' range have manifested relatively synchronous eight- to nine-year cycles of abundance; local fluctuations in eastern ruffed grouse range have been much more erratic.

2. Regional data suggest a well-synchronized eight- to eleven-year ruffed grouse cycle in the Lake States, Ontario, Manitoba, Alberta, and Alaska; and likely in British Columbia, Saskatchewan, and Quebec as well. Ruffed grouse were not cyclic in five eastern states and in the province of New Brunswick.

3. At the continental level, ruffed grouse have exhibited a seven- to ten-year cycle.

4. There are insufficient local indices for prairie grouse, spruce grouse, blue grouse, ptarmigan, and Hungarian partridges to state whether or not they are cyclic; however, the evidence for prairie grouse tends to favor a cycle similar to that of ruffed grouse.

5. Prairie grouse have followed a nine- to ten-year cycle in Manitoba; they are probably cyclic in the Lake States and Alberta, and possibly so in Saskatchewan and British Columbia. Prairie grouse are not cyclic in North Dakota. Ptarmigan are apparently cyclic in Alaska, as are spruce grouse in Manitoba. Fluctuations by the introduced Hungarian partridge have closely resembled those of the ruffed grouse in Manitoba and Alberta, and the partridge in these two provinces can very likely be considered cyclic.

6. The continental population of ptarmigan has undergone an eight- to ten-year cycle corresponding to the cycle of ruffed grouse. Data for spruce, blue, and prairie grouse are limited but strongly imply comparable fluctuations.

7. Snowshoe hare populations on small areas have exhibited broadly synchronous fluctuations indicative of an eight- to nine-year cycle. There has been good agreement between these fluctuations and those of ruffed grouse.

8. Snowshoe hares in the Hudson Bay watershed displayed an eight- to eleven-year cycle during the last half of the nineteenth century. Later regional indices point to concomitant eight- to ten-year oscillations in snowshoe hare populations in all Canadian provinces with the possible exception of the Maritimes, and also in the Lake States. Regional peaks in hares and grouse have occurred about the same time. Snowshoe hare populations of four eastern states are not cyclic.

9. At the continental level, snowshoe hares have generally experienced seven- to twelve-year cycles of abundance and scarcity which are closely aligned with the cycles of grouse and ptarmigan.

10. Muskrats have had a cycle of about eight to ten years in the Mackenzie River District and in Manitoba. This cycle is more irregular than that of hares and grouse.

11. Hudson's Bay Company data indicate a muskrat cycle of around ten years at the continental level, but Canada-wide fur returns since 1919 fail to corroborate this.

12. The lynx has undergone regional cycles of largely nine- to ten-years duration, which have been essentially synchronous for over 100 years. During the present century, the colored fox has manifested an approximate nine-year cycle south of the tundra with a high degree of interprovincial synchronism; coyote populations in the three Prairie Provinces behaved similarly. Mink and fisher are cyclic in Manitoba. There is no evidence of a marten cycle in any of the provinces of Canada.

13. At the continental level, the lynx has followed chiefly a nine- to ten-year cycle for the past 200 years, and the colored fox an eight- to ten-year cycle for at least 100 years. The marten exhibited a cycle of comparable length through much of the nineteenth century but not thereafter. Canadian mink and fisher populations have fluctuated in an eight- to ten-year cycle over the past

four decades, and perhaps during earlier times. The coyote population of the Prairie Provinces has had a nine- to ten-year cycle since at least 1919.

14. The "ten-year cycle" is not found in Europe, but long-term periodicity of about ten years may characterize ptarmigan fluctuations in Greenland and Iceland.

Finally, it is my belief that so long as the term "ten-year cycle" carries no connotation of strict regularity, it serves as a useful description of the nonrandom long-term fluctuations of those North American species noted above.

4

Some population characteristics
of cyclic species

This chapter is devoted to population phenomena which are, or which appear to be, associated with the cyclic propensities of various species; it is also concerned with some of the interrelationships between such species.

Interspecies Chronology
of Ten-Year Cycle Peaks

According to a number of quantitative indices and subjective observations (Table 11), local populations of snowshoe hares have tended to decline after the native grouse. Hares peaked or declined last in sixteen cases, and grouse in four; peaks or declines in both were concomitant but once. Referring to Wisconsin, Leopold (1931, p. 137) noted: "Of 15 cases in which mortality in two or more species was dated in the same locality, ruffed grouse fell off first in eight and prairie chickens first in five. Rabbits were never first. . . ." The maximum difference between local hare and grouse peaks has apparently not exceeded two years, and has been predominantly only one year. Peaks in state and provincial populations occurred first among grouse on eleven occasions, first among snowshoe hares on nine, and were synchronous five times (Table 12). Where the chronology of peaks varied, the average deviation was 1.7 years. Questionnaire data at the continental level show grouse falling before hares three times, and with hares once (Table 9).

Turning to the grouse family itself, there has probably been a tendency for ruffed grouse to peak or decline with or after the other species. This is not only suggested by the reports and indices summarized in Tables 13 and 14, but by subjective appraisals of regional conditions as well. For example, Schorger

(1945), commenting on the situation in Wisconsin during the latter half of the nineteenth century, wrote: "Comparison of the cyclic highs of the ruffed grouse with the cyclic lows of the prairie chicken, as given above, shows that in every case the prairie chicken die-off occurred first." Reports of the chief game guardian or game commissioner for the province of Alberta (Lawton, 1907–31; Anon., 1932; Clark, 1933–36) placed ruffed grouse peaks in 1913, 1923, and 1933, and those of sharptails in 1913, 1922, and 1933. Bradshaw's (1922–27) reports for Saskatchewan indicate a major decline in spruce grouse during 1923, and in ruffed and sharp-tailed grouse during 1926. Yukon ruffed grouse and ptarmigan evidently peaked together in 1915 (Clarke, 1936).

The seeming dependence of the lynx and other furbearers on the snowshoe hare as a staple food was early recognized (see Elton and Nicholson's, 1942b, quotation of Cocking, 1776; also Richardson, 1829, p. 218; and MacFarlane, 1905); and graphic descriptions of lynx starvation following rabbit "crashes" have been given by Seton (1911, pp. 96–98) and Sheldon (1930, p. 329). While the lynx, colored fox, coyote, fisher, and marten cycles are generally believed to have reflected the periodic abundance of their chief prey—the snowshoe hare—this explanation, or at any rate its universal applicability, has been questioned by some workers (Elton and Nicholson, 1942b; Cowan, 1949; Cowan and MacKay, 1950; Butler, 1950, 1953). Here we will deal solely with the observed chronology of population changes.

To what extent movements of predatory furbearers affect numbers locally or regionally is difficult to say. It is evident, however, that lynx have sometimes remained common for one or more years after hares have disappeared (Twitchell, 1921). Lynx were common west of Anzac, Alberta, in the winter of 1955–56 despite the fact that hares have been very scarce since 1953 (Keith, pers. files). Edward Hopegood, one of the area's most successful trappers, told me at the time that when cutting up lynx carcasses for dog food he found their stomachs almost exclusively contained spruce grouse remains. Seton [1929, (1):185], of course, considered the lynx to be the chief enemy of the spruce grouse. On other occasions both hares and lynx have apparently declined together; thus Osgood (1909, p. 80) asserted: "The belief that the abundance of lynxes in a given region is proportionate to the number of hares was borne out by the conditions in the Macmillan [Yukon] region in 1904. Wherever hares were common, lynxes appeared in numbers." Henderson (1923) reported that 980 lynx pelts were traded at Pembina River, Alberta, during the winter of 1906–7, but that the rabbits died off in the spring of 1907 and during the following winter just 40 lynx were brought in.

By comparing Hudson's Bay Company fur returns for the snowshoe hare during 1849–1900 (MacLulich, 1957) with lynx returns from the North Central and James Bay districts of the Northern Department (Elton and Nicholson, 1942b), a picture of hare and lynx fluctuations within roughly the same region is obtained (Fig. 10). Lynx data are complete for both districts during the 1850's and 1860's; in 1858 a major decline took place concurrently among hares and lynx, and in the 1860's the lynx began to decline two to three years after the hares. Lynx figures for the 1870's indicate a peak before or probably at the same time as the one in hares. A major lynx decline occurred in the North Central district during 1887, a year before hares declined in the Hudson Bay drainage as a whole. Lynx populations fell in the James Bay district in 1898; the hares had declined a year earlier. Keeping in mind that very likely the fur returns of predatory species tend to peak later than actual populations, I feel it is safe to conclude that in the Hudson Bay drainage lynx have alternately peaked or declined before, along with, and after snowshoe hares.

Butler (1953) recorded the distribution of "good" years (i.e. "years when peaks are being experienced in various parts of the country . . .") for snowshoe hares and other furbearers in Canada during 1915–53. The initiation of these good years in hare populations preceded that in lynx by one year in three cases, and by two and four years in two others. The termination of good years for lynx averaged three years later than for snowshoe hares. Questionnaire data for all of Canada (Table 9) designated 1933 and 1942 as snowshoe hare peaks, and Dominion Bureau of Statistics records showed 1935 and 1944 as peak years in lynx fur returns.

Because snowshoe hare indices are so limited, the lynx is hereafter used as the reference species for cycle chronology among the predatory furbearers. Butler (1953) compared 106 lynx and colored fox peaks in different sections of Canada from 1915 to 1950; about half the time both species peaked together, while during the other half the lynx was first in about three out of four instances. Thus, on the average, foxes declined 0.3 years after lynx. Butler indicated that the fisher, coyote, and wolf (*Canis lupus*) were even later than the fox, and fur returns from Manitoba, where the fisher is still cyclic, support his findings. Since 1919, Manitoba's peaks in colored fox, fisher, and coyote-wolf pelt collections have averaged 0.3, 1.8, and 2.0 years later than those of the lynx. Within all three Prairie Provinces during this same period, colored foxes and coyotes peaked after lynx by an average of 0.4 and 1.2 years respectively.

Butler noted that the cycles of mink and muskrat, two species often ecologically associated as predator and prey, appeared to be linked more closely to one another than to the cycles of the hare and its dependent predators. Elton (1931) had commented that the muskrat cycle appeared to be inverse to that of grouse and hares, and Elton and Nicholson (1942a) stated: "the muskrat peak precedes by a year or two the main snowshoe rabbit and lynx peaks." MacFarlane (1905) had earlier drawn attention to the only slight dependence of the mink on the snowshoe hare. In 113 of 116 cases examined by Butler, the mink declined with or after the muskrat, the mean delay in mink peaks amounting to 1.4 years.

At the continental level, colored foxes and lynx peaked during the same year eight out of nine times (Table 15). Mink and marten tended to peak before lynx by an average of 1.3 and 2.0 years respectively. The fisher, on the other hand, usually peaked later than the lynx and fox.

Geographic Extent
of the Ten-Year Cycle

The ten-year cycle in North America seems characteristically to be a phenomenon of the northern coniferous forest and its ecotones. Yet, as we have already seen, not all populations of cyclic species within this immense area manifest ten-year cycles of abundance. At present there is no good evidence of regional snowshoe hare cycles within the eastern United States. Similarly, the Snowshoe Rabbit Enquiry revealed poorly marked fluctuations (i.e. a high percentage of "no change" reports) in western mountain regions occupied by *Lepus americanus bairdii* and *L. a. wash-*

ingtonii; and Chitty (1950) concluded: "From a preliminary regional analysis of the whole series of reports, it seems that the rabbit populations in this area [lower third of British Columbia] have shown no widespread regular fluctuations over the past 12 years." Others (Howell, 1923; Banfield, 1958) have likewise expressed the opinion that cyclic fluctuations are not exhibited by insular populations of snowshoe hares in the mountains of the northwestern United States and southwestern Canada.

Ruffed grouse have not been recorded as cyclic in the eastern states or in the province of New Brunswick during the past 20 to 30 years, but there is evidence of a ten-year cycle in this region earlier (Bump *et al.*, 1947, p. 561–566). Perhaps Gordon's (1940) remarks on the effect of forest maturation in Pennsylvania partly explain the current absence of a cycle in the east, although I doubt that they apply to more northerly sections like Maine or New Brunswick, viz., "our forest species of game, such as ruffed grouse and varying hares . . . have suffered from a lack of suitable food and cover. Naturally in such areas their numbers have decreased very noticeably. The varying hare is our best barometer of this changed condition. In former years the kill of these animals was quite high. Now they are almost extinct in large portions of the deer country, and we have no open season for them at this time." Leopold (1933, p. 59) uncovered no suggestion of a cycle, "past or present," in the southern islands of ruffed grouse range in Ohio, Indiana, Illinois, and southern Iowa. Whether the ruffed grouse of the Ozarks were ever cyclic is not known.

Sharp-tailed grouse are not cyclic on the grasslands of North Dakota, and while this species is cyclic in the Prairie Provinces of Canada, the sharptail population there is concentrated mainly in the parkland and marginal-farming sections of the forested zone rather than in the grasslands. Although I have no quantitative information about sharp-tailed grouse fluctuations on the grasslands of the Prairie Provinces, I am familiar with several instances during the last cyclic low when shootable populations existed in southern Alberta and Saskatchewan, while scarcely a bird could be found further north.

It would be extremely interesting to see some good indices for rock ptarmigan — a species that breeds on the treeless tundra but which often winters in the boreal forest. The importance of securing such indices from North America has been greatly increased by the apparently authenticated reports of a ten-year cycle among Iceland rock ptarmigan (Gudmundsson, 1958, and *in litt.*).

Following their analysis of Hudson's Bay Company lynx data, Elton and Nicholson (1942b) concluded: "The cycle covers the whole northern forest zone of Canada, from Labrador to British Columbia and the Yukon. . . . a cycle of about ten years occurs over practically the whole range of *Lynx canadensis*." During the past three or four decades the regularity and conspicuousness of the lynx cycle in Canada seems to have decreased. A number of workers have ascribed this to overtrapping (Butler, 1942; Elton and Nicholson, 1942b; Clarke, 1949; DeVos and Matel, 1952). Butler (1942) submitted that as a direct outcome of intensive trapping, "The population of some of our fur bearers has become so low that they are no longer able to respond to better ecological conditions by an appropriate increase in production."

Elton and Nicholson's statement on the geographic extent of the lynx cycle in Canada is, or was, probably applicable to most other cyclic furbearers. That the colored fox has an approximate nine-year cycle in the forest zone and a fluctuation of around four years on the tundra of northern Quebec and Labrador was demonstrated by Butler (1945, 1951). The so-called three- to four-year cycle in the Far North had, of course, been shown earlier by Elton (1942). Robinson and Robinson's (1946) and Butler's (1951) graphs of colored fox returns from trading posts in the western Arctic also imply short-term fluctuations on the tundra and long-term fluctuations of eight years or more in the forest. Cowan (1938) reported that during the second quarter of the nineteenth century the marten population on the British Columbia mainland had a ten-year cycle, but not on Vancouver Island where snowshoe hares were absent. The fur returns upon which the latter conclusion was presumably based were not presented. Although the marten trade in northern Labrador about this time was very limited, available data definitely indicate short-term fluctuations (Elton, 1942, p. 274). The northern United States has no fur records analogous to those from Canada, hence it is impossible to get a good historical perspective of American fluctuations. The short series of Lake States bounty figures and trapping- and hunting-take estimates commencing in the 1920's and 1930's (Erickson and Burcalow, 1953; Wis. Cons. Dept., 1931–59; L. Eberhardt, *in litt.*) offer no evidence of a cycle in red fox, coyote, mink, or muskrat.

Interregional Chronology of Ten-Year Cycles

It is seldom that a species cycles with perfect synchrony over its entire range, and some indications of systematic progressions of peaks and lows have come to light. During the two cycles covered by the Snowshoe Rabbit Enquiry, for instance, peaks and declines occurred first in Nova Scotia, next in the central part of Canada, and lastly in the Yukon and Alaska. MacLulich (1937) interpreted his questionnaires as showing that in the 1930's "The condition of abundance was reached and passed first in the maritimes, south-eastern Ontario, southern British Columbia, and the Mackenzie delta, and occurred last in the interior of the continent in the northern part of the Canadian life zone and the southern part of the Hudsonian life zone, and in Alaska and Yukon." Actually, his figures, though scanty, place the Alaskan and Yukon peak at least one year later than in the interior. The delayed peaking of snowshoe hare populations in Alaska and the Yukon during the 1930's and 1940's is seen too in a summary of scattered literature reports (Fig. 14). But prior to that time, hare peaks in this region appear to have been largely in step with the rest of the country (Fig. 14).

Using questionnaire data, Butler (1953) mapped the increase of snowshoe hares in Canada, excluding the Maritimes, after the lows of the 1930's and 1940's. He noted that on each occasion the first signs of recovery took place in the northern sector of the Prairie Provinces.

Wing (1960) stated: "In all cycles wherein tested so far, epochs [highs or lows] occur progressively later equatorward. This characteristic behavior is known as *latitudinal passage*." He continued, "It has been noted in the field by a number of naturalists working upon the snowshoe rabbit." It is my opinion that, if anything, current information on snowshoe hares points to just the opposite trend. Wing's attempt to illustrate latitudinal passage by plotting dates of highs and lows in North American rabbits and hares (mainly the snowshoe hare) against latitude is not convincing, and I doubt that analysis of these data would produce a significant regression coefficient.

Speaking of snowshoe hare populations during the 1920's and 1930's, MacLulich (1937) said: "the cycle reached a peak first in south-eastern Ontario and the condition of maximum abundance moved slowly northward, reaching northern Ontario three years later." A reversal of this pattern was claimed by Buckley (1954) for hare and grouse peaks in Alaska, viz., "Although a number of inconsistencies exist, it appears that peak populations and subsequent die-offs occur first in the north and west, with a lapse of up to two years before peaks occur in eastern and/or south-central Alaska."

Bump (1939) compiled reported dates of ruffed grouse abundance and scarcity in eastern Canada and United States from the 1880's to the 1930's, and pointed out that in seven out of eight cases high populations were probably attained first in the North. Bump *et al.* (1947, pp. 567–569) examined information from the same general area since the turn of the century and found no consistent tendency for declines to follow a regular sequence between regions. They further stated that while American data for the 1920's and 1930's fit well the pattern of decrease noted by Clarke (1936) in Canada (viz., a convergence from the northwest and northeast), there had been no such progression in previous cycles.

In his comprehensive review of tetraonid fluctuations, Williams (1954) detected no evidence of a radiating center of decline in North American grouse, though he did conclude that the grouse cycle in the Maritime Provinces was advanced by approximately three years over the main cycle in the remainder of Canada and the northern United States, whereas in Alaska the cycle seemed to be delayed by about three years. However, in view of the irregular fluctuations already noted in New Brunswick's ruffed grouse kill estimates, I seriously doubt that a grouse cycle currently exists in the Maritimes.

With reference to the lynx, Elton and Nicholson (1942b) decided that "There is no regular line of progression or geographical contouring in the incidence of peaks in different regions that can be easily seen when they are mapped in detail. But the results of a rough method of calculation suggest that there is a tendency for the peak to appear first in Athabasca Basin Region and spread west, north, south and east, and to appear last in Lakes and Gulf Regions." Fur returns from the main lynx-producing provinces and territories of Canada (Table N) indicate that during the past four cycles major peaks have usually occurred first in Saskatchewan-Manitoba, second in Alberta-Northwest Territories–British Columbia, third in Ontario-Quebec, and finally in the Yukon. The mean deviation of peaks in the three latter regions from those in Saskatchewan-Manitoba has amounted to —1.8, —2.8, and —3.3 years respectively.

The distribution of red fox peaks in Ontario during three cycles, as shown by Cross (1940), displayed no recurrent pattern. Butler (1953) summed up his views on interregional chronology of cycles as follows:

From the questionnaire data, we conclude that for the three species, snowshoe rabbit, colored fox, and mink, the cycle begins its increase phase in the northern section of the prairie provinces. From this initial area of increase, the reports of increase spread out unevenly in each succeeding year until practically the whole country is covered and the cycle had reached its peak. The decrease phase follows much the same pattern. Muskrats follow the same pattern but deviate from it fairly frequently. The rest of the fur bearers do not follow this pattern but increase more or less independently during the good years. The data do not cover a long enough period since the late 1920's so that one may be sure that each cycle brings forth similar patterns or lack of patterns in the species mentioned above. Nor can we be sure that the reason for the lack of pattern is not an artificial one introduced by the fact that lynx, marten, and fisher are rarely seen whereas snowshoe rabbit and fox are easily seen and their population changes quickly noted.

Amplitude of Cycles

It has become widely accepted as fact that the ten-year cycle displays increased amplitude at higher latitudes. The idea was probably first mentioned by Howell (1923); and, while literature accounts leave one with a strong impression that a marked north-south gradient exists (Dymond, 1947; Rowan, 1950b; Lack, 1954b), present indices, local (Table 16) and regional (Table 17), are inconclusive on this point.

Adams (1959) divided the range of the snowshoe hare into three segments, based on his interpretation of relative differences in cycle amplitude. According to Adams' map, the gradient is mainly north-south in the eastern half of the continent, and northeast-southwest in the western half. I am inclined to believe that there is not enough information at present to justify any such generalization. Indeed, it seems to me that Leopold (1933, p. 64) may have been closer to the truth when he asserted that "Cycles are more severe on large continuous blocks of range than on small, dispersed, or discontinuous blocks," and largely dismissed any notion of a latitudinal effect. Since, by and large, the insular type of hare and grouse range lies to the south, Leopold's statement is not seriously at variance with some of the observations that gave rise to the concept of an amplitudinal gradient. Neither is it untenable with the spectacular fluctuations reported by MacLulich (1937) on his southeastern Ontario study area at Buckshot Lake (see Table 16).

Turning now to amplitude per se, local indices, on the whole, point to wider fluctuations among snowshoe hares than ruffed grouse. None of the nine hare ratios of peak to low populations fell below 13:1, but eight of the twelve ruffed grouse ratios did (Table 16). State and provincial kill estimates, like local indices, showed a considerable range of cycle amplitude both within and between various regions (Table 17). While the figures are not altogether comparable, due to differing geographic origin, the mean amplitude of snowshoe hare fluctuations (6.7:1) exceeded only slightly that of ruffed grouse (6.5:1), which was in turn about one-third greater than prairie grouse (4.6:1).

The amplitude of five consecutive snowshoe hare cycles as recorded in fur returns from posts around Hudson Bay (1849–1904) varied from 960:1 to 6.3:1, and averaged 242:1 (Table 18). Mean amplitudes of lynx cycles in Northern Department districts of Hudson's Bay Company ranged from 222:1 to 18:1, the overall average being 70:1 (Table 18). Recent provincial and territorial fur returns gave overall mean amplitudes of 5.6:1 for lynx, 5.2:1 for colored fox, and 4.3:1 for coyote (Table 19). No peak-to-low ratios were calculated for the colored fox or the coyote in the 1940's, as the unprecedented decline in fur prices after 1944 unquestionably depressed returns far beneath what they might otherwise have been during the low. Similarly, lynx ratios were not calculated from Manitoba and Saskatchewan during this time because of the introduction of trapping restrictions in 1946. The cyclic fisher population of Manitoba had a mean amplitude of 18:1;

for muskrats the mean amplitude was 2.2:1, and for mink just 1.9:1 (Table 19).

Nineteenth- and early twentieth-century fur returns at the continental level yielded mean amplitudes for lynx, colored fox, and marten of 20:1–13:1, 3.4:1, and 2.6:1 respectively (Table 20). Mean amplitudes after 1919 were 3.7:1 for lynx, 2.6:1 for colored fox, and 3.2:1 for mink. Colored fox and coyote amplitudes in the Prairie Provinces averaged 4.9:1 and 3.3:1 during the latter period.

Three general conclusions about cycle amplitude can, I think, be drawn from the foregoing summary: (1) Snowshoe hares fluctuated more violently than ruffed and prairie grouse, (2) lynx fluctuated more violently than the other furbearers, and (3) the amplitude of the lynx cycle at the continental level is currently about one-third to one-fifth of what it was during the nineteenth century, but that of the colored fox has changed little.

Population densities in peak years do, of course, play a key role in determining the amplitude of cycles, but accurate censuses of peak populations have seldom been conducted. The results of all such snowshoe hare and ruffed grouse censuses encountered by me are summarized in Table 16; MacLulich's (1937) summer figure of 3,400 per square mile is the highest recorded for hares, and King's (1937) October figure of 353 per square mile is the highest for grouse. A number of workers have attempted to make reasonably accurate estimates of peak snowshoe hare populations, based on general field observations and extrapolations from small-area counts, etc. These estimates as well as some rough indices are presented in Table 21, and even allowing for a considerable margin of error, there remains little doubt that hares have at times attained prodigious numbers. Rowan's (1954) suggestion of 30,000 per square mile on favorable sites may seem beyond all reason, but I observed this same population — north of the river at Athabasca, Alberta — in the fall of 1952, and saw 52 hares taken in a single drive from approximately 1½ acres of willow (*Salix* spp.) and alder (*Alnus* spp.); at least a dozen others doubled back and escaped the trap. These rabbits were in winter pelage several weeks before there was permanent snow cover, thus facilitating both counting and shooting. A tally of 145 hares along 1 mile of road was made in mid-November, and two of us regularly collected between 15 and 20 per acre of black spruce (*Picea ma-*

riana) muskeg, where they were less numerous but easier to shoot than in the dense alder and willow thickets.

The virtual disappearance of snowshoe hares from large tracts of country during cyclic lows has been almost as striking a phenomenon as their peak densities. I have not endeavored to make a comprehensive survey of population estimates or examples of extreme scarcity during lows, but offer the following by way of illustration:

> One hare per square mile [Seton, 1929, (4):705; MacLulich, 1937; Bailey, 1946].
> One track seen in five days of snowshoeing (Cox, 1936).
> Not a single rabbit seen during a trip down the Mackenzie River (Kindle, 1928).
> Only two snowshoe hares killed all winter despite constant hunting by the Indians (Strong, 1930).

In late August, 1959, at a time when rabbits were reportedly increasing after a low, I drove approximately 250 miles of back roads and trails in the Athabasca district of northern Alberta without seeing a single animal. Twenty-five man hours of intensive searching in excellent snowshoe habitat yielded just three sight records and an extreme paucity of sign.

Reproduction

The term "reproductive rate" is here used to denote the number of young born or hatched per adult female per year, as distinguished from the number present at some later date.

The idea that snowshoe hare litters are largest in peak years and years of cyclic increase was probably first mentioned by Mac-Farlane (1905) and by Preble (1908). While others later echoed the same view (Seton, 1911; Hewitt, 1921; Elton, 1924), MacLulich (1937) was the first to test this hypothesis with series of embryo counts. Contrary to his conclusion, however, litter sizes were not significantly greater during the peak year of 1933 than during the decrease year of 1935 near Smoky Falls, Ontario, viz. 2.67 ± 0.48 *vs.* 2.00 ± 0.43. Yearly means of embryo counts at Aweme, Manitoba, from 1923 to 1935, inclusive, showed no consistent relationship with population fluctuations (Criddle, 1938).

These data did demonstrate for the first time that significant differences may occur between years in the same locality, the mean 2.26 for 1923 being significantly smaller than the means 3.11, 3.60, and 3.71 for 1925, 1926, and 1933 respectively. Green and Evans (1940) reported no significant differences in mean embryo counts between 1932 and 1938 on their Lake Alexander study area. Snowshoe hare populations at Anzac, Alberta, increased markedly during 1949 and 1957, and 1950 was a peak; mean litter size in these three years was 4.06 ± 0.24 (79 litters). Conversely, 1951 and 1952 were years of decline, and in 1956 the population was very low; litter size in these years averaged 2.76 ± 0.69 (17 litters). Numbers were so low during 1953–55 that no pregnant females could be obtained (Keith, pers. files). One can, I believe, safely state that snowshoe hare litter size has sometimes varied significantly between years, but as MacLulich reflected, "whether it was biologically related to the population cycle remains an open question."

Rowan and Keith (1956) detected a tendency for the average litter size of snowshoe hares to increase with latitude. Their summary of the literature has been brought up to date in Table 22, and 95 percent confidence limits computed for mean litter sizes wherever possible. These means fell significantly into three different latitudinal groupings — 60°–66° (4.91), 50°–56° (3.64), and 43°–49° (2.78).

Although doubting that average litter size differed greatly between cyclic stages, Severaid (1942) thought that the average number of litters per female per year likely increased or decreased with snowshoe hare densities. His observations on captive hares had disclosed that females were most receptive to coitus on the day of parturition; he believed the chances of immediate postpartum mating varied directly with the population level, resulting in a lengthening of periods between pregnancies during cyclic lows and thereby reducing the number of litters that the average female could produce yearly. Severaid pointed also to the fact that, since first litters are usually smaller than those born later, the average litter size is apt to be smallest in populations having the least number of litters. The possible compounding effect on the reproductive rate of decreased numbers and sizes of litters during cyclic lows is certainly worthy of further study. To what extent Severaid's postulated influence of low population densities on reproductive rate might be offset by the concentration of hares in nuclei of favorable habitat, a trait discussed shortly, is a moot point.

Rowan and Keith (1956) utilized a technique described by Green and Evans (1940) to calculate the mean number of litters per female per year at Anzac, Alberta, and found that snowshoe hares in northern Alberta produced 17 percent more litters each year than reported from hares in central Minnesota. This, combined with their greater litter size, gave the northern hares a yearly reproductive rate of 54 percent higher than those further south. After perusing references on breeding-season length, Rowan and Keith concluded that the later onset of the breeding period in the north was apparently more than counter-balanced by its later termination.

Yearly observations of clutch size, and egg fertility and viability have rarely been published for cyclic populations of North American grouse. In comparing hypothetical ruffed grouse populations during "normal" years and years of "dying off," Clarke (1936) showed the same number of adults and young as being present at hatching time — implying that he did not consider changes associated with the clutch as an important factor in the decline. Hamerstrom (1939) made the following remark: "Ralph King's well-known but unpublished statement that in Ruffed Grouse there is a marked cycle, inversely synchronized with the population cycle, in the size of the clutch has raised the question for other grouse. . . . There is no significant variation [in prairie chicken clutch size] from the average mid-way in the rise of the cycle (Gross' nests), at the high (Schmidt's nests), or just past the low (Hamerstrom's nests)." Data presented by Hamerstrom likewise indicated fairly constant nesting success among prairie chickens and consistently high egg fertility among both prairie chickens and sharp-tailed grouse.

While I do not regard the ruffed grouse populations studied by Bump *et al.* (1947) as cyclic, this investigation did accumulate a tremendous amount of pertinent nesting information. They determined, for example, that the mean clutch size on three study areas varied by as much as 7 to 11 percent between successive years, and that egg infertility in state-wide populations varied from 1.2 to 7.0 percent. However, there was no apparent relationship between such changes and observed population fluctuations. Egg viability or embryo survival was consistently high. Although they had very little direct evidence, Bump *et al.* concluded that the first year's clutch was smaller than that in subsequent years, and annual differences in average clutch size might therefore result from changed age ratios. Were this true, one would then expect rapidly growing cyclic populations — containing a high proportion of young birds — to have smaller mean clutch sizes than declining populations. The percentage of females that breed each year is an unknown but perhaps important variable.

No one, to my knowledge, has endeavored to collate clutch sizes of North American grouse with latitude, and I doubt whether there are enough records from Canada and Alaska to make an attempt practical. Siivonen's (1954b) capercaillie and blackgame data indicated an increasing clutch from southern to central Finland, then a decrease through northern Finland to Lapland. Westerskov (1956) compared rock ptarmigan clutch sizes in Scotland, Finland, Iceland, and Greenland; these suggested an increase from south to north. Pheasant (*Phasianus colchicus*) clutch size appears to increase with latitude in Europe and the United States (Westerskov, 1956). F. H. Wagner (pers. comm.) recently summarized much of the available information on pheasant clutch size in the United States, and found a statistically significant increase from south to north.

The vicissitudes of the muskrat's habitat — primarily a result of weather and the muskrats themselves — make it essential that any investigation of reproductive rates in relation to this species' cycle be conducted over a long period and preferably at the regional level. Muskrat studies in Iowa, while not dealing with a population whose numerical fluctuations describe a ten-year cycle, nevertheless provide the first good evidence of an underlying long-term oscillation in reproductive rates (Errington, 1954, 1957). Mean litter sizes during the past 20 years have undergone statistically significant changes which tend to be aligned with cyclic highs and lows of northern hares and grouse, though not particularly well with those of northern muskrats (see muskrat fluctuations in Manitoba and Saskatchewan, Fig. 15, for example).

Annual or latitudinal variations in the reproductive rates of predatory furbearers relative to their ten-year cycle have not been investigated. Commenting on the starving lynx population of the Athabasca-Mackenzie region in 1907, Seton [1929, (1):185] wrote: "Not one of them had any Rabbit in its stomach; not one had a bellyful; none of the females were bearing young this year." Noting that martens may decline while rabbits are still abundant, Seton [1929, (1):492] quoted MacFarlane as saying that marten fecundity is reduced both by starvation and overfeeding — the females failing to breed in either case. More recently, Lensink *et al.* (1955) theorized that "The plasticity of the marten's food habits precludes extensive losses from starvation; thus, changes in population levels are probably attributable to altered reproductive success." Although not referring to a cyclic red fox population, Richards and Hine's (1953) observations from Wisconsin are noteworthy: "Changes in the average number of placental sites in red foxes roughly paralleled the population trend. Whether a change in litter size is a mechanism for regulating population size is not known." Significant regional differences in reproductive rates of red foxes in New York were reported by Layne and McKeon (1956), and were attributed to factors associated with "population density" and "carrying capacity." In speaking of the effect of high mouse densities on predators in northern Labrador, Elton (1942, p. 333) speculated: "This outburst of mouse meat undoubtedly spreads a feast for the predatory birds and animals, and must have some effect upon their survival, and perhaps upon their reproductive efficiency." A survey of observations and comments on arctic fox reproduction convinced Braestrup (1941) that litter size varied directly with the short-term fluctuations of this species chief food, the lemming. It is probably reasonable to suspect that an acute shortage of suitable prey could adversely affect the reproductive rates of northern carnivores; possibly such density-related factors as competition for den sites, and intraspecific strife arising from population density per se are also of importance.

The influence of vacillating hare and grouse abundance on the reproductive rates of horned owls and goshawks in Canada has not been subject to immediate field study. Among certain European raptors, both clutch size and nestling survival have varied directly with marked changes in mouse-population densities (Lack, 1954b, pp. 208–209). Lemming and vole fluctuations on the tundra of northern Canada and Alaska probably exercise a similar effect on snowy owl (*Nyctea scandiaca*), short-eared owl (*Asio flammeus*), and rough-legged hawk (*Buteo lagopus*) reproduction (Shelford, 1943; Rausch, 1951; Pitelka *et al.*, 1955; Watson, 1956, Smith and Foster, 1957). Indirect evidence of goshawks experiencing widespread reproductive failures after snowshoe hare declines will be examined shortly.

Mortality

Time of Die-Off. — One feature that has frequently, though not invariably, characterized the ten-year cycle has been a sudden marked die-off of hares and grouse, often spoken of as the "crash." In discussing cycles broadly, Clarke (1949) maintained "one of the most definite things about cycles is 'crash mortality,' where something kills animals and turns abundance into scarcity."

I have assembled eleven reports from the literature (Table 23) which seem to connote crash mortality. These accounts point strongly to midwinter or early spring as the chief period of hare decimation. Further evidence of this is found in some quotations published in the Snowshoe Rabbit Enquiry reports for 1934–36 and 1940–42; 22 of the 26 dated epidemics or sudden declines took place between December and May, and 17 between January and April. The following general statements have also been made: "The Rabbits are wiped out in a single spring by epidemic disease, or diseases, . . ." [Seton, 1929, (4):708]; "death first begins to overtake the rabbits in the fall and hits them on an enormous scale the succeeding spring" (Rowan, 1948).

Green and Evans (1940) felt that the die-off was precipitated by an increase in the mortality rate of young hares from the time of birth until February, and very likely within the first few weeks of their life. MacLulich (1937, p. 120) contended that "nearly all our recorded dead hares and decreases in numbers have been found in summer. . . ." However, he had earlier (pp. 89–90) quoted twelve of his observers, only one of whom mentioned a summer die-off. Eight specified winter or spring, while three others listed fall as the period of marked decline. There was, to be sure, little doubt that the population studied by MacLulich himself at Buckshot Lake, Ontario, suffered heavy mortality during summer, viz. between July and September. One must keep in mind too that the chances of noticing sick or dead hares is probably least in summer when ground cover is dense and decomposition of carcasses rapid.

Shifting our attention now to the ruffed grouse die-off, the predominant opinion seems to be that such mortality manifests itself chiefly in summer and among young birds. Thus we find Phillips (1926) indicating that the cyclic depression of 1924 started immediately after an apparently successful breeding season, and McDonald (1935) referring to an abundance of successfully hatched nests but a dearth of birds by the end of July. Observations by a number of his questionnaire respondents led Clarke (1936) to write: "Certain characteristics of the dying-off are hinted, namely, a heavy loss of young occurring during the summer." Clarke drew the same conclusion from his own Ontario work, and in a stochastic model of a "dying-off" grouse population doubled the "normal" hatching-to-fall mortality rate of young. Boughton (1937) likewise felt that the decline was instigated by increased summer mortality of juveniles while adult mortality remained unchanged.

King (1937) stressed the importance of poor chick survival in the cyclic diminution of ruffed grouse. Census figures given by King enable one to assess the relative significance of seasonal mortality, and do, I think, deserve further attention. From 1930 to 1933 the ruffed grouse population was increasing, and summer (June–October) mortality averaged 59 percent; during these same years, winter (October–April) mortality averaged 25 percent. In the decrease years of 1934 to 1936, summer losses rose to an average of 73 percent, but winter losses rose as well — to an average of 59 percent. Had winter mortality not risen during the decrease years, mean differences between successive spring populations would have been around −34 percent; because there was increased over-winter mortality, mean differences amounted to −60 percent. Taken alone, observed winter mortality rates in years of decrease could have lowered spring populations by about 46 percent, compared to a lowering of just 34 percent due to summer mortality alone. Over-winter mortality must, therefore, have played as great a role in the population decline as did mortality in summer.

After thoroughly combing the relevant literature, Bump *et al.* (1947, p. 573) stated: "Although the evidence points strongly to loss of productivity in terms of birds of the year as the primary manifestation of the forces responsible for the major declines in grouse abundance that have been recorded, adult mortality (apart from that associated with longevity) seems to have been a contributory factor in a number of instances. But the data do not support the conclusion that it may have been controlling." Dorney (1959) reported average fall age ratios of 3.5 young per adult when Wisconsin grouse populations were decreasing, and 4.5 young per adult when they were increasing, thus suggesting above-average summer brood mortality during the period of decline. He witnessed no sudden crash on his study areas and concluded that "gradual increases in juvenile, adult female, and overwinter mortality — all density related — have accounted for the population changes observed."

A fall and winter die-off of ruffed grouse and sharp-tailed grouse was said by Erickson (1938) to have occurred in Minnesota during 1935–36, and Erickson *et al.* (1949) specified that October–December of 1942 was another such period for ruffed grouse. As Rowan (1948) remarked, rapid decomposition of the fragile avian skeleton and very often dense cover greatly reduce the likelihood of encountering grouse remains. Nonetheless, some accounts of dead grouse being found in spring, coincident presumably with cyclic declines, do appear in the literature (Tufts, 1925; Allen and Levine, 1935; Rowan, 1948). A winter die-off of spruce grouse in Labrador was mentioned by Townsend and Allen (1907).

According to Rowan (1948) the crash of Alberta Hungarian partridge populations in 1934 was accompanied by a high rate of juvenile mortality, which resulted in hunting bags containing 70 percent adults (an approximate reversal of the usual age ratio). Cartwright (1944) similarly ascribed the 1942 and 1943 crash declines of Hungarian partridges and sharp-tailed grouse in the Prairie Provinces to heavy mortality of young. An examination of Hungarian partridge age ratios from Alberta (Keith, 1959) suggested that January–March mortality among juveniles had been disproportionately high in 1952 and 1953, at a time when the population was declining; however, sample sizes were small.

Mortality Rates. — Mortality rates of marked snowshoe hares have been calculated in two published studies. Green and Evans (1940) determined that mortality of juvenile hares from birth until

February amounted to 40 percent and 9 percent during two different years of population increase on their Minnesota study area; mortality during four consecutive years of decrease ranged between 71 and 88 percent, and reached 92 percent in the fifth year. Birth-to-February mortality in a declining population of Montana hares was 91 percent (Adams, 1959).

Annual adult mortality rates varied from 64 to 72 percent during four years of population decrease, and rose to 97 percent in the fifth year (Green and Evans, 1940). During the first year of population increase, adult mortality dropped to 59 percent. Adams (1959) computed an adult mortality rate of 78 percent on his Montana study area when the population was falling.

Green and Evans (1940) believed that population declines were initiated after birth-to-February mortality rates of juvenile hares surpassed 70 percent. Similar mortality-rate data remain to be published for other cyclic species.

Die-Off Diseases of Unknown Etiology. — Pathological investigations have shown that snowshoe hares are subject to a variety of infectious diseases — bacterial, fungal, and parasitological (Boughton, 1932; Green and Schillinger, 1935; MacLulich, 1937; Green *et al.*, 1943; Erickson, 1944; Adams *et al.*, 1956). The present section, however, is devoted to a brief consideration of diseases or alleged diseases which may be involved in the cyclic die-off, but whose etiology is currently unknown.

Green and Larson (1938) described a nontransmissible glycogenolytic condition, frequently accompanied by hypoglycemia, which they believed was the immediate cause of death in the cyclic decline of snowshoe hares. They termed this condition "shock disease" and outlined three types of syndromes, viz.: (1) "convulsions are characterized by sudden onset, running movements of the legs, extension of the hind legs, retraction of the head and neck, and absence of foaming at the mouth. During seizures the eyes are fixed, although the corneal reflex is present. Many of the animals go into convulsions by making a sudden violent leap into the air and, upon alighting, develop clonic seizures. Some animals show slight restlessness prior to the onset of grave symptoms, but the greater number abruptly topple over in convulsions. A hare at one moment perfectly normal to all outward appearances may, 5 minutes later, be dead." (2) Symptoms "are associated with a lethargic and even a comatose state." (3) "Some hares go through a sequence showing characteristics of both the above types. . . . The onset is gradual, the symptoms are prolonged, tremors and twitchings are marked, extreme weakness is apparent, and convulsions of long duration finally appear. . . ."

The notable gross pathology centered primarily on changes in the liver and spleen. The liver was described as being darker than normal, exhibiting signs of atrophy, feeling flabby, soft and mealy on palpation, and giving off a sweet nauseating odor. The spleen was dull brown with little blood; the splenic capsule was prominent and covered with many shiny, fibrous threads. Average weights of hares dying of shock disease were 17 percent below normal (Green et al., 1939).

While most of the above information on shock disease came from wild-trapped hares that either died in captivity or in traps, the typical behavior and gross pathological symptoms were said also to have been observed in the wild (Green and Larson, 1938; Green et al., 1938). Indeed, when going through the literature one cannot help being impressed with the similarity between shock disease and the symptoms reportedly associated with a high proportion of deaths in wild hares. If we ignore references to tick infestations, and to boils, lumps, and blisters which almost certainly indicate encysted tapeworm larvae, much of the remaining commentary could well apply to shock disease.

Of the 16 observers whose remarks on hare deaths or sickness were quoted in the Snowshoe Rabbit Enquiry reports for 1934–36 and 1940–42, 7 noted "dopey" or lethargic behavior; 4, convulsions or sudden death; 4, thinness or light weight; 2, peculiar livers; and 3, miscellaneous symptoms. MacLulich (1937) summarized comments by his correspondents on disease during two cyclic declines. In the 1920's, 14 of 28 observers reported hares lethargic, 3 reported hares "sick," and 1 reported a diseased liver; in the 1930's, 29 of 152 observers reported hares lethargic, 33 reported hares "sick," and 8 reported diseased livers. More than likely the term "sick" was simply used to describe sluggish or inactive hares. MacLulich diagnosed stomach worms (Obeliscoides cuniculi) as the cause of the only epidemic among hares studied by him in the field after tests for bacteria, filtrable viruses, and protozoa proved negative; yet, the symptoms manifested by seven hares which supposedly died of stomach worm infections sound strikingly like shock disease, viz. (p. 85): "In the summer of 1935 at Smoky Falls on the Mattagami river recently captured hares began to die, and they had not been mistreated. Of the seven that died six had the stomach full of worms in yellowish thick fluid. The hares did not eat for a day before dying in convulsions. The liver was dark red and congested." Earlier in the same paragraph, MacLulich had stated: "Numbers up to one or rarely two hundred of these blood-sucking worms were found in the stomachs of nearly all the hares autopsied, and may be considered 'normal.'"

The lowered resistance of snowshoe hares to sudden shock or stress, described by Cox (1936) as occurring in high populations and attributed by him to heavy tick infestations, might reflect a condition comparable to that which predisposed Green's captive hares to severe mortality between the fall of 1935 and the early part of 1937 (Green and Larson, 1938). Dead hares found by Porsild (1945) bore no sign of disease, but must have been thin since he mentioned their poor condition and speculated that they may have died of starvation.

Adams (1959) pointed out that the aberrant behavior and occasional death of some hares trapped by him ("trap sickness") resembled shock disease. I too have witnessed this so-called trap sickness, though under different circumstances. In the fall of 1952, immediately prior to a die-off, snowshoe hares were being taken alive near Athabasca, Alberta, by being driven into a large funnel-type trap. It was not uncommon during such drives to see one of the hares ahead of the beaters suddenly go into violent convulsions and die almost immediately. Once in the crowded holding compartment of the trap, many others quickly succumbed without apparent injury. The remaining hares were crated and shipped 100 miles to the University of Alberta but rarely did any survive two weeks of captivity. J. Waring of Anzac, Alberta, attempted to keep small numbers of snowshoe hares in cages and enclosures during the rabbit high of 1949–51, but was largely thwarted by frequent convulsive mortality among his captive animals (Keith, pers. files).

Chitty (1959) challenged the basis for conclusions made by Green and his co-workers regarding the natural occurrence of shock disease in the wild. After critically re-examining the data,

Chitty suggested that shock disease was probably a physiological condition arising primarily from the abnormal stress of trapping and/or subsequent crowded confinement. Chitty's arguments are for the most part well taken and convincing; there are, however, at least two points that definitely need further clarification before shock disease can be dismissed as merely a consequence of unnatural stress. The first, obviously recognized by Chitty and mentioned also by J. F. Bell, is whether a normal liver could have undergone sufficiently rapid degeneration to account for the atrophy and lesions noted in post-mortems of hares dying of shock disease immediately or shortly after trapping. Commenting on this, Chitty maintained (letter dated May 31, 1961): "[one] can find the cellular changes associated with shock disease described in Sir Roy Cameron's 'Pathology of the cell,' Ch. 20. The changes in the liver are the sort of thing that are produced by a variety of agents, and can happen in a matter of hours." The second point is the patent similarity between some of the main terminal symptoms of shock disease, especially sudden convulsive death, and those reported for sick or dying hares in the wild, examples of which were outlined earlier.

Mass die-offs of hares in the Far North have been attributed to a disease whose most obvious manifestations seemingly involve the head and neck region. MacFarlane (1905) spoke of a disease which affected the head and throat and carried off thousands of hares. Preble's (1908, p. 200) oft-quoted remarks may describe the same malady and bear repeating: "A party arriving at Fort Resolution from Hay River in June, . . . reported rabbits extremely abundant, and stated that a large proportion of those shot had accumulations of pus beneath the skin of the neck. Others have reported a similar condition in sick or dead rabbits along the lower Athabasca." He later continued (p. 202): "Throughout the upper Mackenzie region during January, and to a less extent during February, 1904, many thousands of rabbits perished from disease. In some cases death overtook them as they sat in their forms . . . in other cases the animals left the shelter of the woods and after wandering a short time on the frozen surface of the river suddenly sprawled in their tracks and died without a struggle. In the spring when the snow went off many were found in all conceivable positions. . . . When affected, the rabbits become excessively thin. On skinning some which had died of this disease I was at once struck by the dry condition of the skin and flesh, which separated with difficulty. The viscera were in an excessively moist condition. . . . The throat and lungs were much inflamed." There is no way of knowing if the "plague" which swept through the hares on Seton's (1929) New Hampshire estate in 1903 was similar to that in northern hares; the former was diagnosed as a septicaemia due to *Staphylococcus aureus* and appeared outwardly to attack the throat. In the wake of the crash of 1946 in the Mackenzie Delta, Banfield (1951) found three carcasses without significant internal lesions, but examined one sick hare "which had a creamy exudate from the eyes matting the hair of the face."

Behavioral Changes

Habitat Usage. — Habitat usage by snowshoe hares and grouse has been shown to vary with cyclic changes in population density. Thus MacLulich (1937) discovered that in peak years hares tended to be distributed about equally over much of the country, but declined less rapidly in swamps during the crash, and could be found only there during the low. Porsild (1945) described the use of marginal habitat by peak snowshoe hare populations: "During the years of greatest abundance rabbits were plentiful practically everywhere in the delta, even in the treeless but willow-covered northern part. In the mountains west of the delta the species was found from the lowland to the timberline, and even in the treeless Eskimo Lake basin rabbits were occasionally seen in willow and alder thickets along lake shores and creeks." A hypothetical snowshoe hare build-up in, and emigration from, localities having particularly favorable plant successional stages was detailed by Grange (1949) and termed "The Law of Colonization-Dispersal."

An analogous situation to that in hares was outlined by Clarke (1936) for ruffed grouse: "at a low ebb in numbers, the territory occupied . . . represents the best combination of necessary and desirable features to be found in the vicinity, . . . as numbers gradually increase, less and less desirable combinations are occupied. . . . The last territories to be occupied in this process may be called marginal territories and the unoccupied area is uninhabitable for the species." In 1940 the Hamerstroms (1955) rated sections of prairie grouse range near Plainfield, Wisconsin, as "best," "intermediate," and "poorest," and then followed populations on each through the low of 1947. Numbers on the area as a whole decreased by 70 percent; decreases on the best range averaged 60 percent; on intermediate range, 83 percent; and on poorest range, 96 percent. These data thus corroborated Grange's (1950, p. 96) conclusion that "The amplitude of the small game cycle . . . is greatly reduced in perfect habitat. . . . differences in amplitude are observable especially in reference to the depth of the low point of the cycle. In other words, a cyclic population in perfect habitat does not drop in the same percentage as does a similar population in deficient habitat even at the low."

Commenting on upland gamebird distribution in Alberta, Rowan (1948) stated: "When they approach the peak they commonly move into areas in which permanent establishment seems quite unlikely. Sharptails will move onto the prairies, for example, while Hungarians have, during the past two peaks, gone far into the northern wilderness with practically no change of survival or permanent colonization, or westwards right into the Rocky Mountains . . . where the case is equally hopeless for them." Rowan felt too that the small numbers of pinnated grouse which have shown up in Alberta during cyclic highs were immigrants from neighboring Saskatchewan. For some unknown reason these birds tend to concentrate in the immediate vicinity of two or three large shallow lakes. Instances of peak sharp-tailed grouse populations expanding into marginal terrain on the periphery of their range were reported from Alaska by Buckley (1954). Gudmundsson (1958) painted a comparable picture of ptarmigan distribution in Iceland relative to their fluctuations: "In years of abundance the ptarmigan occurs in enormous numbers throughout the country whereas in years of scarcity the population is reduced to very small remnants. . . . In years of increase following a population low these survival 'islands' serve as production centers. From here the birds spread in all directions, gradually populating the whole country. As their numbers approach maximum density, the birds even invade the most adverse environments."

The general pattern that emerges from the above observations is clearly one of cyclic species persisting chiefly in restricted islands or foci of favorable habitat during low years, and dispersing into less favorable habitat as their numbers begin to increase once again.

Mass Movements. — The snowshoe hare is generally acknowledged to be a relatively sedentary species. Seton [1929, (4):704] estimated its customary home range at between 20 and 60 acres, while Adams (1959) found that home ranges of marked individuals on an 80-acre island varied from an average of 13 acres for juvenile males to 25 acres for adult males. Grange (1932) was unable to drive a pregnant female from an area of about 10 acres after 1¼ hours of tracking; 86 percent of Aldous' (1937) retraps were made within ¼ mile of where his hares were initially eartagged; Criddle (1938) believed that the hare's radius of activity ranged from a few hundred yards in dense woods and thickets to a mile or more in open woodland.

Although Seton [1929, (4):729] never observed any sign of a snowshoe hare "migration" and MacLulich (1937) ruled out their occurrence in Ontario during the 1930's, the possibility of mass movements of hares cannot be entirely discarded. Cox (1936) saw what was apparently a sizable emigration of snowshoe hares in northern Minnesota during the peak year of 1912. Of this he wrote:

All the way from Kelliher to the lake [about 12 miles] it was observed that those rabbits in motion all were hopping towards the northwest, and every track in the snow pointed in the same general direction. This aroused my interest, and when Smith and I started across the wide expanse of the lake, rabbit tracks, heading northwestward, continued to be abundant. It was not until we were within 6 or 8 miles of the north shore, however, that we began to encounter rabbits sitting here and there and in groups whenever there were patches of deeper snow on the ice. . . . As we approached the north shore, the animals became more numerous, and I estimated that there were 20 to 50 of them per acre. . . . Rabbits seemed just about as abundant for the first few miles north of the lake as they were south of it. Probably the owls, although gathered here from a large territory, had little effect on the great numbers of rabbits crossing the lake.

During November of 1933, a peak year in Manitoba, Criddle (1938) found the tracks of 17 snowshoe hares that had evidently travelled 8 to 15 miles across a plain in one night. During 1949–57, J. D. Waring, a retired R.C.M.P. constable, and an experienced woodsman, endeavored to record hare movements at Anzac, in the wilderness of northern Alberta. His chief source of information was the number and direction of tracks noted shortly after fresh snowfalls. As a result of these studies, Waring became convinced that frequent mass movements of snowshoe hares occurred through the Anzac district, especially during and immediately following the peak of 1950. The sharply vacillating snaring success of the Indians on a nearby reservation strongly supported this conclusion (Keith, pers. files).

Butler (1953) mapped yearly changes in Canadian snowshoe hare populations and subsequently commented: "The wavelike spread of areas of increase across the country . . . indicates that the first signs of recovery from a cyclic low are seen in the northern parts of Alberta and Manitoba. In succeeding years, reports of increase occur at the fringe of the area reporting increase the previous year, and spread out from this. The easiest biological explanation for these observations would be that as the rabbits increase in numbers they migrate . . . , the direction and the extent . . . depending on population pressure and the current suitability of the habitat encountered."

At least three separate and spectacular emigrations of sharp-tailed grouse have been recorded. Rowan (1948) mentioned a southeasterly flight of sharptails near Chip Lake, Alberta, just before the great peak of 1925. From Rowan's description, 5,000 to 10,000 would be a conservative estimate of the number of birds involved. Snyder (1935) described the mass emigration of obviously many thousands of sharp-tailed grouse from the southern Hudson Bay and James Bay regions of Ontario and Quebec. This movement which took place during October and November of 1932 was associated with peak populations and followed a broad southerly course. Curiously enough, the sex ratio in a sample of 65 specimens was 26:74 favoring females. Snyder believed there was also good evidence of a similar emigration in 1896. He postulated that perhaps psychological unrest due to population density per se, or food depletion — either direct or indirect — helped trigger the 1932 movement. Hanson (1953) thought that sharptails in the Hudson Bay and James Bay regions wintered in heavily wooded areas along watercourses, concentrating there in early fall. He stressed the limited extent of such cover, and suggested that extreme crowding would occur during population highs and might initiate a mass exodus.

Cade and Buckley (1953) gave a graphic account of a sudden emigration of sharp-tailed grouse from the Tanana Valley, Alaska:

"One day in October, 1934, this great number of grouse suddenly arouse en masse and flew off in a great cloud to the south toward the mountains. Mr. Flakne . . . estimated the flock to be two or three miles long, half a mile wide, and in a solid formation several birds deep. . . . No grouse seemed to be left in the area, and nothing was ever learned of the fate of the emigrating birds." If one assumes that the flock was 2½ miles long by ½ mile wide, that the birds were four deep, and that they were an average of 20 feet apart, then a simple calculation places their numbers at about 350,000. Notwithstanding the considerable room for error in such a figure, this must certainly have been a tremendous concentration of sharptails.

Cowan (1955) quoted warden C. J. Phillips as reporting a large influx of sharp-tailed grouse into the lower Athabasca Valley of Jasper National Park, Alberta, during September and October of 1941. The species was at that time experiencing a population high throughout much of the province.

To what extent the sharptail is truly migratory in the Far North, as are willow and rock ptarmigan, is not known; Townsend and Allen (1907) and Preble (1908) both refer to sharp-tailed grouse migrations, however. There appears to be no recent evidence of such movements within the central and southern portion of the species' range, and the situation in earlier times is not too clear (Schorger, 1944; Hamerstrom and Hamerstrom, 1951). Its close relative the prairie chicken, on the contrary, is known to have undertaken extensive annual migrations in the midwestern United States during the 1880's (Leopold, 1931, pp. 173–176; Schorger, 1944), and even as late as the 1930's a winter movement of hen prairie chicken from the northern to the southern half of Wisconsin regularly occurred (Gross, 1930; Schmidt, 1936).

Winter invasions of willow ptarmigan into districts well south of the normal winter range in Canada have often been recorded, and appear to be correlated with high populations in the North (Snyder and Shortt, 1936). A progressive southerly movement of willow ptarmigan, beginning in the winter of 1931–32 and culminating in 1933–34, has been outlined by Snyder and Shortt (1936) on the basis of questionnaire information. Others have likewise reported notable winter invasions, viz.: western Lake Superior region, 1864–65 (Schorger, 1944); Ontario, 1896–97 (Macoun and

Macoun, 1909); north-central Saskatchewan, 1926–27 (Bradshaw, 1927), 1931–32 (Houston and Street, 1959), 1934–35 (Mowat, 1947); southern Manitoba, 1932–33 (Rogers, 1937); and northern Quebec, 1932–33 (Brassard and Bernard, 1937). Occurrences of ptarmigan emigrations during population highs in Alaska were summarized by Buckley (1954).

Emigration was one of the first and most popular explanations among trappers and traders for the periodic scarcity of lynx and marten. While this idea has now been pretty well abandoned, there is still good reason to believe that some of the predatory fur-bearers make extensive movements, particularly after the snow-shoe hare die-off. Hewitt (1921, p. 219) mentioned a southward "migration" of lynx in 1916 and 1917 which brought them into sections of the Prairie Provinces where they had not been seen for many years. I have records of lynx being trapped 30 miles south-east of Edmonton, Alberta, during November 1916 and January 1917. Another such movement took place in 1926 when lynx appeared in the Qu'Appelle Valley of southern Saskatchewan (J. Z. LaRocque, in Bradshaw, 1927). The most recent lynx immigration of which I have knowledge occurred in the Westlock district of north-central Alberta during 1956. It is, I think, doubtful whether there is any real orientation to these movements; they are probably extensive but essentially random. Thus at approximately the same time lynx were turning up in southern parts of the Prairie Provinces, they were also straying as far north as Hudson Strait and Baffin Island (Elton, 1942, p. 436). In the summer of 1907 when lynx were hard pressed for food following a rabbit crash, Seton (1911, pp. 211–212) encountered a starving individual on the Barren Grounds near Artillery Lake, 20 miles from the closest forest. Earlier the same year a lynx was shot 60 miles east of the Mackenzie Delta, and only 10 miles from the Arctic Ocean (Harrison, 1908, p. 238).

Seton [1929, (1):169] cited evidence of a movement of lynx from one district to another 200 miles distant, and Cowan (1938) indicated that extensive mass movements had occurred in British Columbia. A possible seasonal "migration" in Wood Buffalo National Park was reported by Soper (1942). The local Indians believed there was a west-east passage of lynx during December and

January, originating in the vicinity of Caribou Mountain; their trapping success seemed to back this view.

Seton [1929, (2):492] recounted the opinions of some experienced fur traders regarding movements by martens, and concluded that "There are many irregular local migrations and variations of the Marten population, which, however, are not large enough to change materially the regular periodic rise and fall of its aggregate numbers." Cowan (1938) also referred to mass movements of martens, and Clarke (1944) described an apparent emigration: "In the winter of 1942–43 a number of marten (reported to me as 34) straggled out miles beyond the edge of timber to the coastal area near Tuktoyaktuk. One was taken out on the sea ice."

A scarcity of mice and rabbits during the winter of 1927–28 supposedly provoked a large-scale movement of red foxes from Quebec's interior to the Gulf of St. Lawrence coast (Taverner, 1929). Marsh (1938) stated that between 1926 and 1931 only white foxes were traded at Eskimo Point, Northwest Territories, but that red foxes appeared in 1932, and up to 1937 had constituted an increasing percentage of the fur take. Since snowshoe hares peaked during 1933 and were low during 1937 in the forests to the south, it may be that initially population pressure, and later starvation, forced red foxes onto the Barren Grounds. Butler (1945, 1947, 1951) uncovered convincing evidence of widespread colored fox movements. While examining color-phase ratios in fur returns from various sections of Canada, he noted that within limits certain ratios tended to be characteristic of certain regions. At times, however, marked aberrations occurred in these ratios which could not be accounted for genetically, the only possible explanation being a mass influx of foxes having different color-phase characteristics. Field observations which circumstantially pointed to an emigration of foxes were summarized by Butler (1947) as follows: "In the fall of 1942 coloured foxes were extremely abundant at York Factory and relatively scarce at Island Lake 350 miles inland. After freeze-up the fox became exceedingly scarce at York Factory and abundant at Island Lake." Butler ascribed fox movements to population pressures accompanying their periodic increases.

That foxes are capable of traveling great distances from their native haunts is conclusively demonstrated by the numerous extra-limital records of the arctic fox [DeVany, 1923; Seton, 1929, (1):431; Cameron, 1950; Butler, 1953].

Winter invasions of goshawks and horned owls into southern Canada and the northern United States have been reported by many persons; these invasions have occurred at approximately nine- to eleven-year intervals. Spiers' (1939) data indicated that invasion years usually fell one or two years after peaks in northern snowshoe hare populations, but examinations of large numbers of goshawks and horned owls from such flights showed them to be in good condition. This fact seems to have led Spiers to dismiss food shortage as the primary cause of these invasions, and to suggest that they may stem from population build-ups in the North which result in either (1) a larger number, but the same proportion of birds coming south during the course of their normal winter wanderings — and hence being noticed more; or (2) a greater restlessness in the population which actually sends an increased proportion southward. Lack (1954b, p. 209) held that food shortage was clearly responsible for the flights, and asserted that invading birds as a rule leave before they are weakened by starvation. Aside from a few general comments, very little has been published on the food habits of goshawks and horned owls in northern Canada and Alaska; hence their degree of dependency on hares and grouse cannot be definitely stated.

A significant lead as to the cause of these invasions, and one which has been largely overlooked, is the age class of the birds involved. Practically every year small numbers of goshawks move south, and are spoken of as winter residents. Fleming (1907) mentioned that such birds are mainly immatures in years preceding and following the invasion of 1896, but that during 1896 adults predominated. Repetition of this trend during the next invasion (winter 1906–7) is evident in taxidermists' records cited by Deane (1907). Five taxidermists reported receiving a total of 187 goshawks, of which 178 were adults; another received 25–30, nearly all adults. L. J. Eppinger's remarks are of interest because they tend to corroborate Fleming's observations on normal-year vs. invasion-year age ratios. Fleming quotes Eppinger, who wrote: "'Goshawks are very plentiful and seem to be all over this part of the State. Most of them are in mature plumage, while the few which I received last year were all immature birds.'" Goshawks reached California during the invasion of 1916. Three specimens obtained by the California Museum of Vertebrate Zoology and described by Grinnell (1917) were adults; Grinnell also said that 25 others had been seen or taken, and where age was specified all were adults. The University of Wisconsin's trapping and banding program at Cedar Grove, Wisconsin, yielded 31 immature and 4 adult goshawks during the non-invasion years 1950–60 (H. C. Mueller, pers. comm.).

Forbush (1927, p. 119) was the first to interpret the preponderance of adults among invading goshawks as indicative of acute food shortage on the breeding grounds. In this connection he submitted: "Perhaps when food becomes suddenly scarce the hawks rear practically no young. During the summer they can subsist on birds, squirrels and mice, but when the birds go south and snow covers the runways of the mice, lacking rabbits and ptarmigan, the Hawks and Owls must eat each other or starve, unless they migrate."

Although we are not immediately concerned with the snowy owl invasions which occur every three to five years (Gross, 1947), Taverner's (1928, p. 220) statement on the significance of changes in the age composition of owls undertaking southward flights closely parallels that of Forbush. Taverner observed: "This [species] is a winter visitor in the settled parts of Canada. . . . Usually the birds that come from the north are heavily marked juveniles, but occasionally flights occur in which the very white and almost unspotted adults are in the majority. Probably the juveniles are naturally greater wanderers than the adults, which migrate far from their home grounds only when driven out by a scarcity of food." All 13 of the snowy owls aged by Keith (1960) in southern Manitoba during the non-invasion winter of 1957–58 were juveniles, thus providing further testimony that young birds are the normal winter residents.

Since there are no conspicuous plumage differences between immature and adult horned owls, we lack age data relative to their periodic invasions. However, the age-ratio picture for the goshawk is clear-cut and to me constitutes excellent prima facie evidence that food shortages do indeed instigate the major invasions.

Miscellaneous Behavior. — Observations on the seemingly depraved appetites of snowshoe hares during population highs are frequently encountered in the literature. Hares will apparently consume a variety of flesh, especially if it is frozen. Accounts of cannibalism were given by Soper (1921), Seton [1929, (4):717], and MacLulich (1937). Seton [1929, (4):717] also mentioned hares feeding on carcasses of foxes, weasels (*Mustela* spp.), and otters; MacLulich (1937) reported their eating deer (*Odocoileus* spp.) carcasses; and Criddle (1938) described the consumption of a ruffed grouse and part of a horse. In November of 1934, a peak rabbit year, two moose (*Alces americana*) were reportedly killed and cached by a trapper near Whitecourt, Alberta; when this cache was revisited in December all the meat and most of the bones had been eaten — evidently by rabbits (Keith, pers. files). Snowshoe hares have likewise been known to gnaw on creosote-treated telephone poles (Buckley, 1954; Keith, pers. files) and a variety of articles handled by humans (Braestrup, 1940; Soper, 1921), and also to eat sand (MacLulich, 1937; Buckley, 1954) and campfire ashes (Keith, pers. files). One cannot, of course, be absolutely certain that the foregoing behavior occurs only during population highs, for it may simply be more noticeable at such times. Large numbers of snowshoe hares have burrowed into haystacks and died during peak years in Alaska and Alberta (Chitty and Elton, 1937; Rowan, 1948).

Grange (1949, pp. 142–143) believed that hares and grouse are, on the whole, much tamer when abundant than when scarce, and attributed this to the "relatively secure, easy and non-hazardous" life in dense populations. The inference here appears to be that predator-prey ratios are more favorable to prey species during peak years, and that predation pressure on individual hares and grouse is consequently lessened. While verification of this hypothesis must await accurate and concurrent censuses of predator and prey populations together with predator food-habit studies, cycle amplitudes in recent state and provincial indices (Tables 17, 19) offer no indication that predator-prey ratios during peaks and lows differ appreciably. Regardless of what is behind the decreased wariness, I agree with Grange that it is typical. The so-called stupidity of snowshoe hares and grouse during peak years is common knowledge among hunters in northern Canada. I have seen a half-dozen sharptails shot from tree tops without flushing the remainder of the flock; as a youth in Alberta during the summer of 1943, I often bagged ruffed grouse and spruce grouse with a slingshot, and even secured one of the latter with a well-aimed stick. Conversely, during times of scarcity, I have seen small flocks of sharptails that were literally unapproachable, and ruffed grouse as wild as their heavily-hunted counterparts in the eastern United States.

Wastefulness was described by Grange (1949, pp. 143–144) as being characteristic of mammalian and avian predators when prey is abundant. Cox's (1936) account of the slaughter of hares crossing Red Lake, Minnesota, surely supports this view.

Discussing the behavior of central Wisconsin prairie chickens in relation to numbers, Hamerstrom and Hamerstrom (1955) stated that new booming grounds have appeared as populations increased, and established booming grounds have disappeared as populations declined. They also found that the number of successful copulations was related to the number of cocks on the booming ground — tending to be the highest when there were 11–15 cocks present, and to decline when numbers were either larger or smaller.

The salient population characteristics of cyclic species, as categorized and described in the present section, may be summarized as follows:

1. Snowshoe hares have mostly peaked or declined after grouse — at local, regional, and continental levels. Ruffed grouse have tended to peak with or later than other species of grouse.

2. Locally, lynx have at times remained common for two to three years after snowshoe hares have become scarce. Lynx in the Hudson Bay region alternately peaked or declined before, along with, and after hares. At the continental level, peaks in lynx fur returns during both the 1930's and 1940's were two years later than the questionnaire-dated snowshoe hare peaks.

3. There has been a tendency for colored fox peaks in regional indices to occur slightly later than lynx peaks; coyotes and fisher have peaked still later. Mink fluctuations appeared more closely associated with fluctuations of muskrats than of snowshoe hares. Continental populations of lynx and colored foxes peaked together eight out of nine times; mink and marten usually peaked before lynx, and fisher after.

4. While the ten-year cycle may be restricted to the northern coniferous forest and its ecotones, areas of such forest in the western mountains (from the lower third of British Columbia southward) and in the eastern United States do not, by and large, support cyclic snowshoe hare populations. A comparable situation presently exists for ruffed grouse in the eastern United States and in the province of New Brunswick.

5. Cyclic increases and decreases have not, on the whole, followed a consistent geographic pattern. Certain broad generalizations can be made, however: Snowshoe hares and possibly grouse declined first in Nova Scotia, and last in the Yukon and Alaska during the 1930's and 1940's; declines elsewhere in Canada fell between these extremes. During the same period, cyclic increases of hares, colored foxes, muskrats, and mink in Canada, excluding the Maritimes, began in northern sections of the Prairie Provinces. Nineteenth-century lynx peaks tended to occur first in the Athabasca Basin. Provincial fur returns for lynx since the 1920's have usually peaked first in the Manitoba-Saskatchewan region.

7. Although snowshoe hare litter size increases significantly with latitude, existing indices do not support the belief that cycle amplitude is well correlated with latitude per se.

8. Snowshoe hare indices have fluctuated more violently than those for ruffed grouse and prairie grouse, and lynx indices more violently than those for the other furbearers. Amplitudes of recent lynx cycles at the continental level have been about one-third to one-fifth of what they were during the previous century, but those of the colored fox have changed little.

9. Peak densities of 1,000 or more snowshoe hares per square mile have been commonly attained in the northern and central parts of the species' range.

10. Litter sizes of some local snowshoe hare populations have varied significantly between years; however, there is no clear-cut evidence that such variations were tied directly to their ten-year cycle. Changes in reproductive rates of cyclic predators are suspected, though not proven.

11. The most noticeable die-offs among snowshoe hares have generally taken place in late winter or early spring. Heavy juvenile mortality in summer seems largely responsible for past ruffed

grouse, sharp-tailed grouse, and Hungarian partridge declines, but winter mortality has been noted as well.

12. A single study's data indicated that mortality rates of juvenile snowshoe hares were, for the most part, higher and more variable than adult mortality rates when populations were declining. This higher juvenile mortality was also revealed in another investigation.

13. Symptoms resembling those of "shock disease" have often been observed in the wild during snowshoe hare die-offs. The overt symptoms of another die-off disease apparently involve lesions on the head and neck.

14. Cyclic species tend to persist in scattered nuclei of favorable habitat during periodic lows, and to disperse from these into less suitable habitat as populations increase.

15. Mass emigrations associated with population highs have probably occurred among snowshoe hares, and have been witnessed among sharp-tailed grouse and willow ptarmigan. Lynx, colored foxes, and marten have almost certainly undertaken similar movements. Food shortage and population pressure are the most frequently postulated reasons for such phenomena.

16. The abnormal paucity of juveniles in the periodic winter invasions of goshawks strongly suggests that food scarcity first causes a reproductive failure and later forces the adults to emigrate.

17. A number of behavioral changes have been noted during population highs, viz., depraved appetites of hares, tameness of hares and grouse, wastefulness by predators, etc.

5

Hypotheses of cycle causes

Theories on causes of cyclic fluctuations have been grouped and discussed by other workers under several broad headings. Hutchinson (1942) commented: "If we have a real periodicity, it may presumably be due to cyclical events outside the ecosystem or to the generation of cycles by mechanisms inside the biological system." Hutchinson and Deevey's (1949) later classification of cycles as "extrinsic" or "intrinsic" seems to re-express this same view. The terms "extrinsic" and "intrinsic" were likewise used by Lack (1954b) to describe factors and mechanisms of alleged cyclic importance. Cited extrinsic influences appear to be mainly climatic or meteorological, and have thus sometimes been referred to as "cosmic," "extra-terrestrial," and "extra-mundane."

Solomon (1949) spoke of "overpopulation theories," "enemy-prey oscillations," and the "meteorological theory" in connection with cycles. I have employed part of Solomon's classification in the following discussion, but as a result of publications by Palmgren and Cole, one more category was added, viz., the "random-fluctuations theory." I do not intend to cover the entire spectrum of ten-year cycle hypotheses, nor do I wish to offer still another theory on a subject already surfeit with speculation but sorely lacking in field research. My aim is simply to outline a representative sample of the more notable theories, and, where possible, to examine these in light of current information on cycles as reviewed in the preceding sections. The order in which hypotheses are considered is not consciously a reflection on their relative merit; it represents largely a chronological sequence within the above-mentioned categories.

Random-Fluctuations Theory

Palmgren (1949) pointed out that mean intervals in series of random numbers — such as might be obtained by throwing a die — resembled mean intervals in the short-term fluctuations of some northern European birds and mammals. He suggested, therefore, that these short-term fluctuations were attributable to random fluctuations in certain "master factors," probably climatic. The similarity between mean intervals in random series and those in actual population series was strengthened when the former were serially correlated. Palmgren justified this step by likening it to the carry-over effect of one year's population level on that of the year following.

Palmgren's argument was restated by Cole (1951) who wrote: "If, as is known to be the case, many factors operate to favor population change, we might expect the resultant of the many haphazard influences to appear as essentially random fluctuations." Cole (1951, 1954) then compared mean intervals in various population indices with mean intervals in truly random data, and concluded: "such population cycle data as we have today are consistent with the hypothesis that population changes are initiated by purely random fluctuations in environmental conditions," and "until definite evidence to the contrary is forthcoming, the preferred interpretation of population cycles should be that they are essentially random fluctuations with serial correlation between the populations of successive years." In a later publication, Cole (1957) remarked: "I am convinced that the burden of proof has been handed back to those field workers who persist in seeing something mysterious in the fluctuations of natural populations."

The mean-interval approach, augmented with empirically calculated confidence limits, was utilized earlier in the present paper as one means of identifying nonrandom fluctuations in population indices. Contrary to Cole's assertions, there are a number of indices — local, regional, and continental (Tables 4, 6, 7, 8, 10, and in text) — which indicate, beyond any reasonable doubt, long-term nonrandom fluctuations. Despite his claim to rigid objectivity, Cole seemingly elected to use some of the poorest available indices [i.e. Poland's (1892) lynx data and Elton and Nicholson's (1942a) muskrat data] in order to repudiate the existence of a ten-year cycle. Other biologists have expressed the same concern about Cole's work (Rowan, 1954; Williams, 1954). While I believe that the poorer indices should indeed have been tested for randomness, a fair appraisal of cyclic phenomena patently cannot rest wholly on the analysis of these data alone.

The great value of Cole's work goes almost without saying: he unquestionably prompted critical reinspection of data that previously passed as cyclic; he has, in part, provided us with a quick check for randomness in population series; and by re-emphasizing the dangers inherent in data smoothing, the possibilities of nonsense correlations, and the invalidity of ordinary tests of significance for time-series comparisons, he has evoked an awareness of some of the pitfalls besetting cycle analysis.

Meteorological Theories

Theories here classified as "meteorological" are those in which meteorological factors constitute the dominant guiding force. Their effect on cyclic populations may or may not be direct, however.

The first of the meteorological theories to gain notoriety was offered by Elton (1924), who pointed out that cyclic peaks of snowshoe hares in Canada had been fairly closely associated with sunspot minima since 1845. Elton emphasized the improbability of changing solar radiation having a direct effect on animals, but mentioned the likelihood of an indirect effect through plants. While submitted only as an hypothesis deserving further investigation, the sunspot theory was accepted by many persons, and more than a decade passed before available hare and lynx indices were compared statistically with the sunspot series (MacLulich, 1937). Although the tests employed by MacLulich were apparently not strictly valid for time-series data, his conclusion that the ten-year cycle and the sunspot cycle are unrelated was perfectly correct (Moran, 1949).

Disproval of the sunspot theory did not prevent formulation of other radiation-based theories. Huntington (1945, pp. 492–507) believed that the ten-year cycle was correlated with an ozone cycle in the lower atmosphere of comparable length. He indicated that ozone — formed through ultraviolet light bombarding upper-atmosphere oxygen — settles into the troposphere, but is quickly removed in the tropics by strong oxidative processes which are less intense further north. Ozone thus tends to accumulate in polar regions, and is carried equatorward in air-mass movements. Huntington stressed the reputed physiologically stimulating effect of ozone on northern plants and animals and suggested that these populations wax and wane with long-term variations in ozone levels. As noted by Huntington, two objections to his ozone theory are (1) the lack of experimental evidence of ozone's effect, and (2) the European source of ozone-level data, whereas the ten-year cycle is a North American phenomenon. To these objections must be added the questionable nature of the techniques used for measuring ozone levels, the absence of a clear-cut ozone cycle without a great deal of smoothing, and the short time span of the ozone series (about 30 years). Moreover, while Huntington thought that the ozone cycle was a global phenomenon, there is no evidence of a ten-year cycle in northern Europe, even among the congeneric and conspecific relatives of North America's cyclic mammals and birds.

Rowan (1950a, 1950b) interpreted the above-mentioned ozone records in an entirely different manner. He felt these readings reflected upper-atmosphere ozone — a strong absorber of ultraviolet light — and that the observed periodicity could produce a ten-year fluctuation in ground-level ultraviolet. Spring readings of upper ozone at the Arosa Observatory, Switzerland, during 1927–29 and 1932–50, tended, in Rowan's opinion, to corroborate the ozone phase of his hypothesis. Rowan believed the biological significance of ultraviolet light to be far greater than that of ozone, and postulated that long-term variations in ultraviolet, combined with the virtual absence of ultraviolet during winter in northern latitudes (Gowan, 1948), could have important biological ramifications. He thought that a deficiency of ultraviolet might act directly upon the animals themselves, but more probably through their plant foods; the effect might also be cumulative and predispose cyclic species to all kinds of diseases because of nutritional imbalance. According to Rowan (1950b), the above hypothesis explained the ten-year cycle's persistent intervals regardless of population densities, the continental, and perhaps circumpolar extent of the cycle, its restriction to high latitudes, the seeming adoption of cyclic behavior by the introduced Hungarian partridge and ring-necked pheasant in western Canada, and the failure of migratory and insect-eating birds to manifest the cycle.

Buss (1950) challenged Rowan's thesis on the grounds that the ozone series covered too short a period and was also incomplete; Buss further thought Rowan incorrect in ascribing a ten-year cycle to the pheasant. The first point is, I think, well taken; there are insufficient indices for western Canadian pheasant populations to comment on the second. By and large the criticisms leveled previously at Huntington's ozone theory apply equally well to Rowan's upper-ozone ultraviolet hypothesis. Leopold and Ball (1931) concluded that the lack of synchronism between British and American grouse fluctuations ruled out cycle theories based on solar radiation. Williams (1954) similarly argued that if some "extra-terrestrial" factor was behind North American grouse cycles, we should then expect to find greater intra-regional synchrony, and no time lag such as appears to exist between the Maritime Provinces, the rest of Canada, and Alaska.

Among the earliest speculated causes of periodic decimations, especially of ruffed grouse, were abnormal weather conditions during winter or spring (see Bump et al., 1947, p. 13–17, for a synopsis); and the idea of climatic control of grouse and hare populations is still popular. Thus in concluding his review of tetraonid fluctuations, Williams (1954) stated that weather systems were probably important in synchronizing population changes over large areas. He cited Chitty's (1952) view that widespread favorable years could elevate low populations while maintaining those already high, and that widespread unfavorable periods could bring all populations down together. If certain weather systems are to be regarded as the primary cause of cycles, then one must, of course, demonstrate a comparable periodicity in their occurrence. If, however, they are to be considered only as occasional synchronizing agents, then we are really no closer to a solution of the cycle's basic periodicity.

Grange (1949, p. 193) expressed the belief that "The most basic cause of animal cycles, in fact, is the interacting force of climatic and plant succession cycles." As I see it, Grange's thesis is that cyclic fluctuations in rainfall — closely tied to sunspot activity — result in a cyclic recurrence of forest fires. These in turn initiate secondary successions which, after several years, provide ideal food and cover conditions for snowshoe hares. The ensuing population explosion sets up pressures that lead to dispersal and to colonization of adjacent but less favorable habitat. Forest growth on the burn continues, the surviving trees become taller, the cover sparser, and the accessible bark less palatable; eventually the habitat deteriorates to such an extent that the hares must emigrate, starve, or be eaten by predators. Though in Grange's (1949, p. 140) own words, "*it really makes little or no difference which fate surplus individuals in a declining habitat meet*. . . . The salient point to be made is that *the habitat itself has declined with respect to available natural resources until the formerly abundant population can no longer be supported within it*." According to Grange, post-fire successions also favor ruffed grouse, but grouse declines are caused by fluctuating predation pressure stemming largely from a predator shift following the hare crash. In the absence of suitable prey the predators ultimately die through starvation.

Much of the ecological thinking behind Grange's theory is undoubtedly sound; nevertheless, as Hickey (1955) noted, the fundamental difference in periodicity between the sunspot and ten-year cycle constitutes a formidable argument against the former's controlling the mechanism of the latter. Grange (1949, p. 128) acknowledged that discrepancies and conflicts existed between these two cycles, and later (p. 195) commented: "Perhaps the greatest unsolved riddle of the northern small game cycle is why this has shown, for the last century, an apparent regularity of about ten years, whereas the sunspot cycle shows no such regularity, and averages slightly more than eleven years. Obviously, the two cycles do not coincide entirely; there remains a distinct and important gap in our understanding of such details. This technical point (and a considerable number of others) must await further research." If one is prepared to accept the theory that the sunspot cycle governs rainfall which in turn governs forest fires and hence plant successions, one can hardly dismiss the discrepancy between the sunspot and ten-year cycle so lightly. I for one am perfectly willing to recognize the cogent effect of post-fire successions, but until proof of a ten-year periodicity in the incidence of forest fires is forthcoming, there seems little reason to subscribe to Grange's hypothesis.

Butler (1953) attributed the characteristic periodicity and synchrony of the snowshoe hare cycle to the chance combination of numerous favorable factors (many of which are connected directly or indirectly to weather), and to emigration from areas of highest densities. The association between cycles of different species implied to Butler the presence of an "external agency" acting similarly on each. The cyclic decrease was simply described as "density-dependent." While there is no definite proof one way or the other regarding hare emigrations, it is difficult for me to envision how, even with emigrations, the random combination of many favorable environmental factors could produce the undisputable regularity of the ten-year cycle. Moreover, the postulation of an external factor tending to synchronize fluctuations of various species is barely compatible with the concept of a density-dependent decline.

The "lunar theory" proposed by Siivonen and Koskimies (1955) is founded on the assumption that each species has a critical period, during which its future reproductive potential may be importantly affected by the quantity of moonlight to which it is exposed. This critical period allegedly coincides with the final stages of the gonad's seasonal recrudescence. Because the lunar month is just 29.5 days, the 12 lunar months total only 354.4 days, or 10.9 days less than the calendar year. The lunar cycle in any one year is thus advanced 10.9 days over the preceding year. If one determines, over a number of years, the date on which any one day in the lunar month falls nearest any given critical date, one finds that about every 8 to 11 years (average 9.6 years) the particular lunar day occurs within ±1 day of the critical date. There is, in my opinion, no good reason why this theory should be considered anything more than an example of how some data may be manipulated to produce nonsense correlations. As the authors freely admit, there is no experimental justification for this hypothesis, and so far as I know the results of their proposed follow-up studies have not been published. Actually Siivonen (1957) has apparently discarded the lunar theory as an explanation for the fluctuations of European tetraonids in favor of another based on "spring phenology."

Elton and Nicholson (1942a) were convinced that the muskrat cycle in Canada was controlled by some over-riding climatic factor; and the alignments of Iowa muskrat data with phases of the ten-year cycle in the North prompted Errington (1957) to venture: "I think my data *could* be consistent with something like changes in ultraviolet radiation, as such investigators as Rowan [1950b] and Shelford [1951] have proposed." Elton and Nicholson (1942b) conceded that the lynx cycle appeared to be tied to that of the snowshoe hare, but did not entirely discount the possibility of a common factor affecting both species, a belief likewise expressed by Rowan (1950b) and Butler (1953). Certainly the occasional decline of lynx before hares (Fig. 10) is at variance with a strict predator-prey relationship. In such instances, epidemic disease or large-scale emigrations may be involved. Cowan (1949), for example, reported a disease-caused decline among colored foxes in the Mackenzie Delta at a time when hares were still plentiful. Emigration of predators from an abundant food supply seems a much less credible explanation. In a summary statement, Elton and Nicholson (1942b) wrote: "We have at present no clue at all to the nature of the factor controlling this enormous wild-life rhythm in the northern forests, except that it seems almost certain that climatic fluctuations must play a controlling part." Clarke (1936) designated a blood parasite, *Leucocytozoon bonasae*, as the immediate cause of a ruffed grouse decline in Ontario, but said: "if a general parallelism is found between the abundance of grouse and that of hares, some external factor, not the cause of dying-off but one influencing rather the general trend of the cycle, must be sought to explain it." That such a general parallelism does indeed exist can surely no longer be questioned. Though evidently favoring a predator-prey oscillation theory of the Lotka-Volterra type, Moran (1953) remarked: "it is hard to study the whole series of trapping records without feeling that there is some very powerful external influence at work."

The continuing popularity of meteorological theories doubtless stems from the extraordinary regularity and synchrony of the ten-year cycle. Neither of these features is commonly observed in wildlife fluctuations, and that both should occur together seems particularly remarkable. In general, meteorological theorists believe that biological systems are so infinitely complex as to rule out the chance of an intrinsically produced ten-year cycle.

Overpopulation Theories

The gist of overpopulation theories is that some species increase in density within their normal environment until levels are attained which trigger overpopulation phenomena, viz., disease, starvation, physiological imbalance, emigrations, etc. These factors quickly reduce populations to low levels once again, and the pattern is repeated.

Seton's [1929, (4):708–710] account of the rabbit cycle as a steady increase to spectacular numbers, inevitably followed by a devastating "plague," clearly belongs among the overpopulation theories. MacLulich's (1937) interpretation of the cycle mechanism was more refined but essentially the same as Seton's. MacLulich believed that the snowshoe hare cycle was best described as a "relaxation oscillation" [a gradual logistic increase and a sudden precipitous decrease (Gause, 1934)]. Epizootics of varying etiology were presumed to have caused hare crashes. The recurrence of cycles of similar length supposedly "depends chiefly on the time the population takes to grow from scarcity to abundance, following the logistic or sigmoid curve of growth, and secondly on the time required for the relaxation reaction. The relaxation oscillation takes a short time because a slow acting infection would, except by a rare chance, be outstripped and supplemented by a faster acting epidemic infection."

MacLulich's explanation for the persistent regularity of cycle lengths is contingent on the assumption that different snowshoe hare populations consistently require about the same period of time to increase from scarcity to abundance, following which density-related epizootics suddenly appear and quickly reduce abundance to scarcity. Considering the known or suspected effects of habitat type, weather, population density, and other variables on rates of population growth and on disease outbreaks, I do not see how the foregoing assumption could possibly be realized in nature. Nor is there anything in this hypothesis to account for the broad synchrony of local and regional population cycles. At the onset of declines local hare densities have varied greatly — both between areas during the same cycle, and between cycles on the same area. MacLulich estimated peak densities at 3,400, 1,200, and 300 per square mile on three of his study areas during 1932 and 1933, while peak densities ranged from 478 per square mile in

1933 to 160 per square mile in 1941 on Green's Lake Alexander study area (Table 16). This suggests to me that populations may often have declined in spite of, rather than (as MacLulich infers) because of, existing densities. Rowan's (1950b) observations in Alberta led him to emphasize the apparent independence of crashes on densities per se; King (1937) had arrived at the same conclusion regarding ruffed grouse declines in Minnesota.

Dymond (1947) presented another cycle hypothesis: "Briefly the theory here offered to account for the periodicity in the fluctuations of the populations of lemmings, hares, voles, grouse, etc., is that the biotic potential of these animals is definitely greater than the normal resistance of the environment in which they live. In other words they are endowed with too high a reproductive capacity and it is the monotony or relative uniformity of the Arctic and far northern environment that accounts for the regularity with which they increase to the unstable level of numbers which brings about the periodic decline." Dymond noted that it is the regularity of the decline which has to be explained; he considered disease and emigration as the normal decimating factors.

An adequate assessment of Dymond's ideas is difficult because of the vague terminology in which they are framed. If he spoke of environmental monotony and uniformity in largely a physiognomic sense, then to attribute the regularity of the ten-year cycle to this cause seems entirely unrealistic to me. What, for instance, could appear more uniform or monotonous than the grasslands and deserts of western North America; yet there is, to my knowledge, no good evidence that rodent, lagomorph, and grouse fluctuations in these great regions ever approach the regularity of the ten-year cycle. On the contrary, sharp-tailed grouse are non-cyclic on the prairies of North Dakota (Fig. 6), and the white- and black-tailed jack rabbits (*Lepus townsendii* and *L. californicus*) of the plains are notoriously irruptive — population increases evidently being favored by low rainfall and overgrazing (Mohr and Mohr, 1936; Bronson and Tiemeier, 1959). Sage grouse indices are insufficient to establish the character of this species' fluctuations. Patterson (1952, p. 35) was inclined to think of cyclic fluctuations as occurring in Wyoming, but opinions solicited by the "Western States Grouse Questionnaire" (Gullion, 1954) proved conflicting.

In a later section of his paper, Dymond ascribed the basic periodicity of cycles "to the essential stability of the environment of animals of high biotic potential whose habits tend to insulate them from extreme climatic conditions." While this escape from climatic extremes may be true for some Microtinae, it is hardly a valid description of the habits of hares and grouse. An additional shortcoming of Dymond's theory, like that of MacLulich (1937), is its inability to cope with the tendency toward repeated and widespread synchronization of cyclic peaks and lows.

Selye's General Adaptation Syndrome provided the basis for Christian's (1950) cycle hypothesis. Christian suggested that wild animals in high populations experienced increased stress due mainly to lack of food and cover, greater predation pressure, and intraspecific strife. The purported adaptive responses by individuals to these stresses were believed to bring about an overall lowering of resistance to disease and parasites. The principal cause of population declines, however, was thought to be "Exhaustion of the adreno-pituitary system resulting from increased stresses inherent in a high population, especially in winter, plus the late winter demands of the reproductive system, due to increased light or other factors. . . ." In support of this theory, as applied to the ten-year cycle, Christian pointed out that symptoms of adreno-pituitary exhaustion closely resemble those reported by Green and Larson (1938) for hares dying of shock disease, and that recorded die-offs have predominately occurred in winter or early spring. Differences in peak densities were ascribed to differences in the carrying capacity of the habitat, while some synchronization of peaks over limited areas was thought to be achieved by major climatic upsets.

During the past decade, Christian and his associates have conducted an impressive array of laboratory experiments with confined rodents (mainly *Mus*) populations. Summarizing this and related work, Christian (1961) maintained that social pressures or stresses, initiated by increasing population density and acting through the central nervous system, had been shown to produce the following basic effects: "increased adrenocortical activity, depression of reproductive functions . . . , inhibition of growth, inhibition of sexual maturation, decreased resistance to disease, and inhibition of growth of nursing young with effects on subsequent generations, apparently through deficient lactation." Christian further concluded on the basis of current information that wild populations of several rodent and lagomorph genera, including *Lepus* "regulate the sizes of their populations largely through internal behavioral-physiological interactions."

While there is, as Christian indicated, evidence that populations of certain species have been importantly affected in the wild by stress-induced density-dependent changes in reproduction and mortality, other evidence, from both field and laboratory, tends to controvert any extensive generalization about the role of such a mechanism in the natural control of populations. Anderson (1961), for example, compared the social structure, behavior, and adrenal and reproductive responses of "feral," "field commensal," and "experimental" populations of *Mus*. He concluded that the social hierarchy observed in experimental populations was primarily an artifact of abnormally high density combined with lack of escape cover and opportunity to emigrate; and thus the attendant "gonadal-adrenal-pituitary relationship explored by Christian . . . would be involved only rarely" in regulating natural populations. Negus *et al.* (1961) also emphasized the artificiality of densities and environmental conditions in Christian's experiments, and noted that adrenal response, even to extreme crowding, had been small compared to that observed in the wild and attributable to changing climate, food supply, or reproductive state. Interpreting the results of their own investigations, Negus *et al.* commented: "The rise and fall of the *Oryzomys* population on Breton Island and the coincident change in adrenal weights can clearly be interpreted in the light of Christian's theory of socio-psychological stress. But is there not an eqally valid hypothesis on the basis of our data? We can just as well explain the increase in adrenal size and complete cessation of reproduction, as well as weight loss in the population, on the basis of climate and food." Wodzicki and Roberts (1960) studied wild rabbit (*Oryctolagus*) populations of different density and, although increased adreno-cortical activity accompanied higher densities, the later did not "lead to any noticeable stress but, on the contrary seem[ed] to improve the rabbits' condition as shown by fat deposits."

Lack (1954b, p. 213–214) criticized Christian's (1950) attempted relation of the ten-year cycle to metabolic derangements, arising from crowding, on the grounds that: (1) the decline would be expected to terminate once numbers had fallen, not to continue for four or five years, thereby involving individuals never exposed to crowding; (2) the decline would start with the same degree of crowding each time, instead of at a wide range of population densities; and (3) adaptations would have developed to counteract this type of mortality. One objection to Lack's second criticism is that the intensity of stress resulting from crowding might theoretically be influenced by density-independent factors operating on the habitat; and his third argument is obviously true only as long as such mortality does not in the long run have survival value. Lack's first criticism seems well taken, for it is hard to explain why unstressed local populations should continue to decrease after attaining relatively low levels. Nevertheless, Chitty (1955, 1957) has contended that adverse affects of crowding and mutual strife among voles may later be manifested in their descendants by decreased viability and other deleterious characteristics. An experiment comparing the "emotionality" of progeny from stressed and unstressed pregnant female rats (*Rattus*) suggested that maternal anxiety could be passed *in utero* to offspring (Thompson, 1957). As with the overpopulation theories already discussed, a fundamental weakness of Christian's hypothesis is its failure to account for the typical synchrony of the ten-year cycle.

Lack (1954a) proposed still another theory: "It is suggested that the basic cause of cycles is the dominant rodent [in this case the snowshoe hare] interacting with its vegetable food to produce a predator-prey oscillation. When the rodents decline in numbers, their bird and mammal predators . . . prey upon and cause the decrease of the gallinaceous birds . . . and themselves die of starvation and/or emigrate." The notion of a cycle-producing interaction between dominant rodents and their impinging vegetation had earlier been expressed by Hutchinson and Deevey (1949) in reference to Elton's (1942) book: "Hidden in his text there are essentially three suggestions. One of these is based on the great modification of vegetation by abundant rodents, and implies in fact a Volterra-Lotka cycle between the animal population and the plant community."

Cycle regularity was credited by Lack to the inherent rhythmicity of the rodent-vegetation interaction, which was likened to a predator-prey oscillation. Interregional synchronization was thought perhaps due to emigration. Features of cycles that Lack interpreted as indicative of a rodent-vegetation interaction were (1) several generations of decline, (2) reports of cover denudation, (3) heavy juvenile mortality, (4) emigration, and (5) regularity. Other workers would patently interpret some of these points differently. Since there have been no good quantitative or qualitative studies to date on the effect of snowshoe hare populations on their food supply, this aspect of the present hypothesis can neither be refuted or verified. I am, however, inclined to agree with Koskimies (1955) that serious quantitative destruction of vegetation by hares, though occurring at times, is probably exceptional. Recent lemming research in Alaska (Thompson, 1955; Pitelka, 1957) has, nonetheless, tended to support Lack's hypothesis as it pertains to the short-term fluctuations of these arctic microtines.

The second part of this theory, viz., that the grouse decline is brought about by a predator shift following the hare die-off, is, as Lack acknowledges, not a new idea (see Cabot, 1912; Burnham, 1918; Hewitt, 1921; Cox, 1936; and Grange, 1949). If the foregoing assumption is correct, one would normally expect hares to decline prior to grouse in any one area. As evidence that such is the case, Lack cited kill records for the Lake States showing that hares fell before grouse on seven out of eight occasions, the eighth being doubtful. Hoffmann (1958) was skeptical of the predator-shift explanation for grouse declines and listed a number of instances in which grouse had decreased first. When interspecies chronology of cycle peaks was reviewed earlier in the current work (Tables 11, 12) the conclusion was reached that snowshoe hares have tended, if anything, to decline *after* grouse at local, regional, and continental levels. The predator-shift hypothesis is thus untenable as a generalized account of grouse declines. Naturally, this is not to say that snowshoe hare predators never aggravate or initiate decreases in grouse populations.

Lack's opinion that the cyclic declines of predators are basically caused by food shortage has, of course, long been widely accepted as fact. It is supported by direct field observations and much circumstantial evidence. Of the latter, wolf (mainly coyote) pelt collections in Canada over the past 140 years are, I think especially indicative. For as Hewitt (1921, pp. 224–226) pointed out, extermination of the plains bison (*Bison bison bison*) during the 1870's was not only followed by a drop in wolf fur returns, but also by a transition from highly irregular fluctuations to fluctuations having major peaks at roughly ten-year intervals. We have already seen (Figs. 19, 23) that from 1915 (when Hewitt's data terminate) to the present time coyote fur returns have been strikingly cyclic. The most plausible explanation for this shift to cyclic fluctuations appears to be that extirpation of the bison sharply reduced timber wolf numbers and caused a greater proportion of the coyote population to become dependent on snowshoe hares as a staple diet, particularly during periods of hare abundance; and that with the periodic declines of hares many of these predators starved or failed to reproduce. Interspecific predation and even cannibalism might play a considerably more important role in cyclic decimations of some mammalian predators than is currently acknowledged. Seton (1929), for example, mentioned that young coyotes and colored foxes are eaten by timber wolves and the larger birds of prey, while adult foxes are preyed upon by wolves, coyotes, lynxes, and fishers. He stated further [(1):188]: "The Lynx is the deadly foe of the Fox and habitually kills it when there is soft snow and scarcity of easier prey." Cannibalism by a lynx was recently reported from Ontario (Elsey, 1954).

As mentioned earlier, several prominent investigators have not, however, entirely discounted the possibility of both predators and prey being affected by a common cyclic influence.

Other Theories

In a recent paper, Lauckhart (1957) submitted that animal cycles might stem from cyclic changes in the nutritive quality of certain key plant foods. A similar view has been expressed from time to time by other workers, especially those seeking a link between animal cycles and meteorological phenomena (King, 1937; Braestrup, 1940; Rowan, 1950b), but Lauckhart's theory differs from the latter in that nutritional fluctuations are largely attributed to processes inherent in the plants themselves. This hypothesis is based on the knowledge that some forest trees and shrubs exhibit seed cycles, i.e., they tend to store up nutrients in their tissues over a period of years and then deplete these reserves in a single season by producing a heavy seed crop. Lauckhart believed that buds, twigs, and bark are nutritionally marginal at best, and that this periodic loss of nutrients renders them incapable of providing many herbivores with an adequate supply of necessary food elements, thereby lowering resistance to environmental stresses and decreasing reproductive rates and survival of young. While the most common mean interval between seed years is reportedly about 3.5 years, Lauckhart felt that the interaction of two or more seed cycles could result in much longer animal cycles. He apparently failed to note, however, that among the species listed by Baker (1950, p. 192) as having essentially annual seed crops with little yearly variation were those constituting the staple diet of snowshoe hares and northern grouse, i.e. jackpine, willows, aspens, and poplars. Another important food plant, birch, was said to have a good seed crop every two to three years. In summarizing the European work on this subject, Baker (1950, p. 191) also indicated that uniformly good seed crops over areas the size of Montana would be rare. If Baker's information is correct, it would seem that Lauckhart's theory can scarcely be given serious consideration as an explanation for the ten-year cycle.

Following a statistical analysis of Hudson's Bay Company fur returns for lynx, Moran (1953) remarked: "the data are at least consistent with the idea that the cyclic behaviour is due to factors intrinsic to the biological system." He later concluded: "our findings are consistent with the view that the cause of the cycle is the predator-prey relationship of the lynx and the rabbit and that the synchronization is due to weather." Moran mentioned two difficulties with his suggestion that the lynx-hare cycle is an intrinsic oscillation of the Lotka-Volterra type, viz., (1) the synchronous fluctuations of animals not ecologically dependent on snowshoe hares, and (2) Elton and Nicholson's (1942b) report that the introduced hares on lynx-free Anticosti Island were apparently cycling in unison with those on the mainland. Though certainly a special case, snowshoe hares on Valcour Island, New York, declined in 1944, well after the virtual elimination of all predators (Crissey and Darrow, 1949).

A further objection to Moran's hypothesis is that lynx have been practically extinct throughout most of south-central Alberta and Saskatchewan, and southern Manitoba for the past 25 years, yet the snowshoe hare cycle persists in this region. There are undoubtedly other places in Canada where the same situation holds. A strong case against Moran's theory can be made by comparing snowshoe hare and lynx fur returns. Normally there is little commercial demand for hare pelts in Canada, and comparatively few are marketed each year. However, when the Australian rabbit supply was cut off during World War II, American felt manufacturers turned to Canada. In 1942, at least 8.8 million snowshoe hares were pelted in Alberta and Saskatchewan (Rowan, 1948; E. L. Paynter, *in litt.*), and according to Rowan the Alberta take "barely scratched the surface of the hare population." Lynx peaked a year later and a total of 1,814 pelts were obtained from these two provinces. Assuming that these fur returns were equally representative for both species, the hares outnumbered the lynx in the wild by 4,900 to 1. This is probably an extremely conservative estimate since a far higher percentage of the lynx population than of the hare population must have been harvested. It is inconceivable, therefore, that lynx could have caused the hare decline.

I am convinced, and assuredly many others are as well, that none of the foregoing hypotheses can adequately account for the ten-year cycle. Those salient characteristics of the cycle that have proved most difficult to explain may be summed up as follows:

1. The restriction of the ten-year cycle to North America (Iceland may be an exception) though the same or closely related animal species occupy very similar habitat in northern Europe.

2. The cycle's further restriction within North America to the northern coniferous forest and its ecotonal communities.

3. The broad synchronization of the ten-year cycle over a vast continental area extending from Quebec through Ontario, the Lake States, the Prairie Provinces, and into northern British Columbia and the Northwest Territories.

4. The persistent cyclic interval of largely eight to eleven years.

5. The essentially concurrent cycling of both snowshoe hares and native grouse, and the apparent adoption of this same cycle by the introduced Hungarian partridge in parts of western Canada.

The ten-year cycle is not likely to become better understood by further theorizing. Clearly the present need is for comprehensive long-term investigations by a diversified team of specialists. The significance of such studies was appropriately expressed by Rowan (1950b) who declared: "As a phase of animal conservation, there is probably no single aspect of greater importance on the North American continent than solution of the ten-year cycle."

6

Summary

This work attempts to outline the current status of our knowledge on the alleged ten-year population cycles of certain northern birds and mammals. Previous usage of the term "cycle" to describe population fluctuations is reviewed and, for the present analysis, it is arbitrarily decided to restrict this term to nonrandom fluctuations with mean intervals between major peaks of around ten years. The main limitations and biases in various types of relevant population indices are considered briefly.

Population indices for species purported to manifest ten-year cycles of abundance are examined at local, regional, and continental levels. When of sufficient length, population-index series are tested for randomness by comparing their mean intervals (between all peaks) with those in serially correlated random series of similar length — confidence limits having been calculated empirically for the latter. Major peaks are selected subjectively.

This appraisal of available indices led to the following tentative conclusions (the term "ten-year" is used here in a broadly descriptive sense without any implication of precise periodicity):

1. The ruffed grouse has exhibited a relatively synchronous ten-year cycle at local, regional, and continental levels over most of its range — known exceptions being the eastern United States, and the province of New Brunswick in Canada.

2. Regional populations of prairie grouse are cyclic in Manitoba, probably cyclic in the Lake States and Alberta, and possibly so in Saskatchewan and British Columbia. Ptarmigan in Alaska and spruce grouse in Manitoba also have a ten-year cycle. The Hungarian partridge is likely following a ten-year cycle in Manitoba and Alberta. The continental population of ptarmigan has exhibited cyclic fluctuations similar to those of the ruffed grouse;

and combined spruce grouse, blue grouse, and prairie grouse data strongly imply comparable fluctuations.

3. With the exception of hunting-kill estimates from the eastern United States, available snowshoe hare indices point to a ten-year cycle at local, regional, and continental levels that is well aligned with the grouse cycle.

4. Mackenzie River District and Manitoba pelt collections show a ten-year cycle in muskrats. A continental ten-year cycle is suggested in Hudson's Bay Company fur returns, but not in recent Canada-wide fur returns of the Dominion Bureau of Statistics.

✳ 5. Regional lynx populations have undergone essentially synchronous ten-year cycles of abundance for over 100 years. Similar ten-year cycles have likewise occurred in colored fox and coyote populations in Canada during at least the present century. Mink and fisher are cyclic in Manitoba, but there is currently no evidence of a marten cycle in any province.

6. Canadian lynx and colored foxes have followed a ten-year cycle at the continental level for the past 200 and 100 years respectively. The marten had a comparable cycle through much of the nineteenth century but not thereafter. Mink and fisher in Canada have displayed a ten-year cycle over the last 40 years and possibly longer. This is also true of coyotes in the Prairie Provinces.

7. The ten-year cycle is not present in Europe, but a similar periodicity may characterize ptarmigan fluctuations in Greenland and Iceland.

8. So long as the term "ten-year cycle" is used with no connotation of strict regularity, it serves as a useful description of the nonrandom long-term fluctuations typical of the above-mentioned species.

An examination of the interrelationships and population characteristics of these cyclic species prompted a number of additional conclusions (as employed in the following, the term "peak" refers to a major peak):

1. Snowshoe hares have tended to peak slightly later than grouse at local, regional, and continental levels, while ruffed grouse have tended to peak along with or later than other grouse.

2. Locally, lynx have sometimes remained common two to three years after snowshoe hares became scarce. Lynx in the Hudson

Bay region alternately peaked or declined before, along with, and after hares. At the continental level, peaks in lynx fur returns during both the 1930's and the 1940's were two years later than questionnaire-dated hare peaks.

※ 3. Colored fox peaks in regional indices have usually occurred slightly later than lynx peaks; coyote and fisher peaks have occurred still later. Mink fluctuations seem more closely tied to the fluctuations of muskrats than to those of snowshoe hares. Continental populations of lynx and colored foxes peaked concurrently eight out of nine times; mink and marten usually peaked before lynx, and fisher after.

4. The ten-year cycle is apparently restricted to the northern coniferous forest and its ecotones, though at the present time much of the southeastern and southwestern extensions of this great plant formation evidently do not support cyclic grouse and hare populations.

5. While, for the most part, there has been no consistent geographic pattern to cyclic increases and decreases, certain generalizations are permissible. During the 1930's and 1940's, snowshoe hares and grouse declined first in the Southeast (Nova Scotia) and last in the Northwest (Yukon and Alaska); cyclic declines elsewhere in Canada, and in the Lake States, occurred between these extremes. During the same two decades, cyclic increases of hares, colored foxes, muskrats, and mink in Canada, excluding the Maritimes, began in northern sections of the Prairie Provinces. Nineteenth-century lynx peaks tended to occur first in the Athabasca Basin; provincial fur returns for lynx since the 1920's have largely peaked first in the Manitoba–Saskatchewan region.

6. Available indices do not support the contention that there is a direct correlation between latitude per se and cycle amplitude.

7. Snowshoe hares have fluctuated more violently than ruffed grouse, which have in turn fluctuated more violently than prairie grouse. Lynx fluctuations have been more extreme than those of other furbearers. The amplitude of recent lynx cycles has declined markedly, while that of colored fox cycles have changed little.

8. Most die-offs of snowshoe hares have been recorded in late winter or early spring, and observed symptoms in dead or dying hares have frequently resembled those of "shock disease." Summer mortality among juveniles seems chiefly responsible for ruffed

grouse, sharp-tailed grouse, and Hungarian partridge declines, but winter mortality has apparently been involved as well.

9. Cyclic species tend to persist in scattered nuclei of favorable habitat during lows, and to disperse from these areas into less suitable habitat as populations increase.

10. Large-scale emigrations of sharp-tailed grouse and willow ptarmigan, probably contingent upon population highs, have been witnessed. Comparable mass movements have likely taken place among snowshoe hares, lynx, colored foxes, and marten. Age-ratio data strongly imply that the periodic winter invasions of goshawks are initiated by acute food shortage.

The principal cycle hypotheses are classified into four main groups, viz., the "random-fluctuations theory," "meteorological theories," "overpopulation theories," and "other theories." Hypotheses advanced to date are patently open to criticism (sometimes severe) on the basis of existing information about the ten-year cycle. None of these hypotheses is wholly satisfactory, and only through a concerted research effort is the true explanation for this cycle likely to be found.

✦✦

Text Tables
Appendix

TABLE 1

Mean intervals or average cycle lengths in different-length series of random numbers with full serial correlation [1]

Series length	No. of series examined	Mean length of all intervals	Mean interval for each series		
			Total range	$\geqq$ 98% of range	$\geqq$ 95% of range
20	100	3.80	2.33–11.00	2.33–6.00	2.33–5.33
33	60	3.90	3.00– 7.25	3.00–5.50	3.00–4.80
50	40	3.91	3.23– 5.11	3.23–4.88	3.23–4.60
100	20	3.92	3.41– 4.74		3.41–4.27

[1] Determined empirically by serially correlating 2,001 random numbers listed in Fisher and Yates (1948).

TABLE 2

Comparison of observed (parentheses) and predicted distributions of intervals or cycle lengths in four sets of different-length series of random numbers with full serial correlation[1]

Interval length	Percentage distribution of interval lengths			
	N = 20	N = 33	N = 50	N = 100
2	(15.5) 12.6	(13.5) 11.9	(13.0) 11.6	(13.1) 11.3
3	(32.8) 31.6	(32.5) 30.7	(32.8) 30.3	(32.3) 29.9
4	(24.0) 29.0	(24.4) 29.0	(23.8) 29.0	(24.1) 29.0
5	(18.1) 15.4	(18.2) 15.9	(19.1) 16.1	(18.8) 16.3
6	(5.9) 7.4	(6.7) 7.9	(6.1) 8.1	(6.8) 8.3
7	(2.3) 2.7	(2.5) 3.0	(3.1) 3.2	(3.0) 3.3
8	(0.6) 1.0	(1.5) 1.1	(1.3) 1.2	(1.3) 1.2
>8	(0.8) 0.4	(0.7) 0.5	(0.7) 0.5	(0.6) 0.6
No. series examined	100	60	40	20
Mean length of all intervals	(3.80) 3.87	(3.90) 3.93	(3.91) 3.96	(3.92) 3.98

[1] Observed distributions calculated from a table of 2-digit random numbers given in Fisher and Yates (1948, pp. 104–105). Theoretical distribution calculated from formulae given by Cole (1954, Appendix I). Percentage distribution of cycle lengths carried to one decimal point beyond statistical significance.

TABLE 3

Approximate 95 percent levels of significance for mean intervals in different-length series of random numbers [1]

Series length	Approximate 95% level of significance for mean intervals
20–25	5.4
26–28	5.0
29–32	4.9
33–40	4.8
41–49	4.7
50–61	4.6
62–73	4.5
74–94	4.4
>94	≤4.3

[1] Interpolated from data in Table 1, column 6.

TABLE 4

Distribution of interval lengths in Hudson's Bay Company snowshoe hare pelt collections [1]

Interval length (years)	Hudson Bay Watershed	
	MacLulich (1937)	MacLulich (1957)
2	2	—
3	3	2
5	3	2
6	3	2
7	1	—
8	—	1
11	—	1
Total intervals	12	8
Period covered	1847–1904	1849–1904
Mean interval	4.4	5.9
Approx. 95% level of sig.	4.6	4.6

[1] Figures given by MacLulich (1957) were revised from the earlier data. Thus according to MacLulich: "For the years 1863, 1872, and 1883 . . . the skins from Moose River and East Main did not reach England until one year late and were included in next year's sales. To avoid unwarranted conclusions about minima or peaks in these years, the figures for each pair of these years have been averaged . . . ."

TABLE 5

A synopsis of peak years in snowshoe hare populations as indicated by three different questionnaires

Province or territory	Peak years as interpreted from questionnaires					
	MacLulich (1937)		Elton et al.[1]		Rowan (1953)	
Yukon	— —	— —	1935	1944	— —	— —
Northwest Territories	— —	— —	1934	1942	— —	— —
British Columbia	1923	1932	1934	1943	— —	— —
Alberta	— —	1933	1933	1941	1942	1953
Saskatchewan ⎫			1933	1941	— —	— —
⎬ 1923	1933					
Manitoba ⎭			1933	1941	— —	— —
Ontario	1923	1933	1933	1942	— —	— —
Quebec	— —	1931	1933	1942	— —	— —
New Brunswick	— — ⎫		1932	1943	— —	— —
⎬ 1931						
Nova Scotia	— — ⎭		— —	1940	— —	— —

[1] Interpreted from information obtained by the Snowshoe Rabbit Enquiry (Elton, 1933, 1934; Elton and Swynnerton, 1935, 1936; Chitty and Elton, 1937, 1938, 1939, 1940; Chitty and Chitty, 1942; Chitty and Nicholson, 1943; Chitty, 1943, 1946, 1948, 1950).

TABLE 6

Distribution of interval lengths in Hudson's Bay Company muskrat pelt collections (data taken from Elton and Nicholson, 1942a)

Interval length (years)	Mackenzie River District	Total for Northern Department
2	1	2
3	2	3
4	3	3
5	2	2
6	5	2
7	—	1
8	1	—
10	—	1
Total intervals	14	14
Period covered	1849–1927	1821–1891
Mean interval	4.9	4.6
Approx. 95% level of sig.	4.4	4.5

TABLE 7

Some recent mean intervals (years) in provincial and territorial fur returns (data from Dominion Bureau of Statistics and various provincial government sources)[1]

Province or territory	Muskrat	Lynx	Colored fox	Coyote	Mink	Fisher
British Columbia	– –	3.8	4.7	– –	– –	3.4
Alberta	– –	3.7	5.8*	5.0*	– –	– –
Saskatchewan	4.2	3.6	8.5*	4.1	3.6	– –
Manitoba	5.0*	7.3*	6.5*	5.0*[2]	4.5	5.8*
Ontario	3.5	6.8*	3.5	– –	– –	4.7
Quebec	– –	9.3*	– –	– –	– –	4.3
New Brunswick	– –	– –	3.1	– –	– –	– –
Nova Scotia	– –	– –	5.2*	– –	– –	– –
Yukon	– –	4.3	– –	– –	– –	– –
Northwest Territories	– –	4.8*	– –	– –	– –	– –

[1] Fur returns cover last 34–44 years and are presented in Tables L, M, N, O, P, Q; asterisk (*) denotes a significant difference from mean intervals found in random fluctuations (95% level of significance about 4.8).

[2] Includes timber wolf.

TABLE 8

Distribution of interval lengths in Hudson's Bay Company lynx pelt collections (data taken from Elton and Nicholson, 1942b)

| Interval length (years) | Total catch | | Catch in Northern Department districts | | | | | | |
	Poland (1892)	Hewitt (1921)	Mackenzie River	Athabasca Basin	West Cent.	Upper Sask.	Winnipeg Basin	North Cent.	Total
2	3	1	--	--	--	1	--	2	--
3	3	1	2	--	--	--	1	1	--
4	4	--	1	--	--	--	--	1	--
5	3	1	1	2	--	--	--	--	--
6	--	--	1	1	1	--	--	1	--
7	3	1	--	--	--	1	1	1	--
8	--	--	--	1	1	--	1	--	--
9	3	2	4	1	2	3	2	2	4
10	4	4	4	3	3	2	2	1	2
11	--	--	--	--	--	--	--	1	--
Total intervals	23	10	13	8	7	7	7	10	6
Period covered	1751– 1889	1821– 1911	1821– 1934	1821– 1891	1821– 1891	1821– 1891	1821– 1891	1821– 1891	1821– 1891
Mean interval	5.8	7.5	7.5	7.9	8.9	8.0	8.0	6.3	9.3
Approx. 95% level of sig.	<4.3	4.4	<4.3	4.5	4.5	4.5	4.5	4.5	4.5

TABLE 9

Peaks and lows in Canadian populations of snowshoe hare, ruffed grouse, and ptarmigan

Snowshoe hare [1]		Ruffed grouse [2]		Willow and rock ptarmigan [2]	
Peak	Low	Peak	Low	Peak	Low
– –	1929 [2]	– –	1928	– –	1929
1933	1937	1932	1937	1933	1935
1933 [2]	– –	– –	– –	– –	– –
1942	1945	1939	1946	1941	1947
– –	– –	1949	– –	– –	– –

[1] Interpreted from information obtained by the Snowshoe Rabbit Enquiry (Elton, 1933, 1934; Elton and Swynnerton, 1935, 1936; Chitty and Elton, 1937, 1938, 1939, 1940; Chitty and Chitty, 1942; Chitty and Nicholson, 1943; Chitty, 1943, 1946, 1948, 1950).

[2] Interpreted from information obtained by the Hudson's Bay Company Zoological Reports, and the Canadian Arctic Wildlife Enquiry [see Williams (1954) for grouse data, and Elton and Swynnerton (1936) for hare data].

TABLE 10

Some recent mean intervals (years) in Prairie-Province and Canada-wide fur returns [1]

Species	Prairie Provinces	Canada
Muskrat	– –	3.9
Lynx	– –	5.8*
Colored fox	8.7*	9.0*
Coyote	7.3* [2]	– –
Mink	– –	5.8*
Fisher	– –	5.5*
Marten	– –	3.7

[1] Except for mink and colored fox, mean intervals given under "Canada" were computed from data in the *Canada Yearbook*, issued annually by the Dominion Bureau of Statistics; mean intervals for mink and colored fox were computed from a graph of Canada-wide fur returns (Butler, 1953). Colored fox and coyote mean intervals given under "Prairie Provinces" were computed from provincial fur returns. Data cover last 32–39 years; asterisk (*) denotes a significant difference from mean intervals found in random fluctuations (95% level of significance about 4.8–4.9).

[2] Includes timber wolf from Manitoba.

TABLE 11

Some reported relationships between major peak years or initial years of decline in local populations of snowshoe hares and grouse

State or province	Locality	No. times hares peaked or declined before grouse	No. of years before	No. times hares and grouse peaked or declined in same year	No. times grouse peaked or declined before hares	No. of years before	Source of reference data
		RUFFED GROUSE					
Saskatchewan	N. of Prince Albert	- -	- -	- -	1	- -	R. F. Huber, *in* Bradshaw (1923)
Manitoba	Aweme	2	1, 2	- -	1	1	Criddle (1930); Lloyd (1936); Criddle (1938)
Wisconsin Ontario	Ladysmith	- -	- -	- -	1	- -	Grange (1936)
	Buckshot Lake	1	2	- -	- -	- -	Clarke (1936); MacLulich (1937)
	Bigger Lake	- -	- -	- -	1	1?	
	Frank's Bay	- -	- -	- -	1	1	
British Columbia	Atlin	- -	- -	- -	1	- -	Swarth (1936a, 1936b)
Minnesota	Cloquet Forest	- -	- -	- -	1	½	Morse (1939)
Alberta	"Several"	- -	- -	- -	1+	- -	Elton and Swynnerton (1935) quoting Rowan
Wisconsin	Bayfield Co.	- -	- -	- -	1	1	Buss and Buss (1947)
New York	Valcour Island	- -	- -	1	- -	- -	Crissey and Darrow (1949)
Manitoba	Riding Mt. Natl. Park	- -	- -	- -	1	1?	Soper (1952a, 1953)
Minnesota	Cloquet Forest	- -	- -	- -	1	1	Marshall (1954)
		PRAIRIE GROUSE					
Manitoba	Aweme	1	1	- -	2	1, 2	Criddle (1930); Lloyd (1936); Criddle (1938)
Manitoba	Riding Mt. Natl. Park	- -	- -	- -	1	1?	Soper (1952a, 1953)
		SPRUCE GROUSE					
British Columbia	Atlin	- -	- -	- -	1	- -	Swarth (1936a, 1936b)
Saskatchewan	Prince Albert Natl. Park	- -	- -	- -	1	2	Soper 1951b, 1952b)
Grand Totals		4		1	16		

TABLE 12

Relationships between major peak years in state and provincial population indices of snowshoe hares and grouse

State or province	No. times hares peaked or declined before grouse	No. of years before	No. times hares and grouse peaked or declined in same year	No. times grouse peaked or declined before hares	No. of years before	Source of reference data
			RUFFED GROUSE			
Wisconsin	3	1?, 1, 4	--	--	--	Figs. 2, 11
Michigan	2	3, 3	--	--	--	Figs. 2, 11
Minnesota	--	--	--	1	1	Figs. 2, 11
Alaska[1]	--	--	--	2	2, 1?	Buckley (1954)
Alberta	½[2]	--	1½	1	1	Table 7; Rowan (1953); Clarke (1936)
Saskatchewan	--	--	--	1	1	Table 7; Clarke (1936)
Manitoba	--	--	--	1	1	Table 7; Clarke (1936)
Ontario	--	--	1	1	1	Table 7; Clarke (1936); Fallis (1945)
Quebec	½	--	½	--	--	Table 7; Clarke (1936)
Totals	6		3	7		
			PRAIRE GROUSE			
Wisconsin	2	2, 2	--	--	--	Figs. 6, 11
Michigan	1	1	1	--	--	Figs. 6, 11
Minnesota	--	--	--	1	3	Figs. 6, 11
Alberta	--	--	1	1	1	Rowan (1953)
			PTARMIGAN			
Alaska	--	--	--	2	1?, 1	Buckley (1954)
Grand Totals	9		5	11		

[1] Includes also sharp-tailed grouse, blue grouse, and spruce grouse.

[2] One-half value assigned when one questionnaire showed peaks in same year, while another indicated that hares peaked first.

TABLE 13

Some reported relationships between major peak years or initial years of decline in local populations of ruffed grouse and other grouse

State or province	Locality	No. times ruffed grouse peaked or declined before others	No. of years before	No. times ruffed and other grouse peaked or declined in same year	No. times other grouse peaked or declined before ruffed	No. of years before	Source of reference data
		PRAIRIE GROUSE					
Saskatchewan	N. of Prince Albert	1	3?	--	--	--	R. F. Huber *in* Bradshaw (1923, 1925)
Manitoba	Aweme	--	--	1	2	3, 1	Criddle (1930)
Saskatchewan	Yorkton	--	--	1	--	--	Houston (1949)
Manitoba	Riding Mt. Natl. Park	--	--	1	--	--	Soper (1953)
		SPRUCE GROUSE					
Saskatchewan	Emma Lake	--	--	--	1	1?	Mowat (1947)
Saskatchewan	Prince Albert Natl. Park	--	--	--	1	--	Soper (1952b)
Alaska	Lower Yukon	1	--	--	--	--	Brandt (1943)
Totals		2		3	4		

TABLE 14

Relationship between major peak years in state and provincial population indices of ruffed grouse and other grouse

State or province	No. times ruffed grouse peaked or declined before others	No. of years before	No. times ruffed and other grouse peaked or declined in same year	No. times other grouse peaked or declined before ruffed	No. of years before	Source of reference data
PRAIRIE GROUSE						
Wisconsin	– –	– –	1	1	2	Figs. 2, 6
Michigan	– –	– –	– –	2	2, 3	Figs. 2, 6
Minnesota	1	1	– –	– –	– –	Figs. 2, 6
Manitoba	– –	– –	1	2	1?, 1	Figs. 3, 7
Saskatchewan	– –	– –	1	– –	– –	Figs. 3, 7
Alberta	1	1	1	– –	– –	Rowan (1953)
British Columbia	– –	– –	– –	1	1	Figs. 3, 7
SPRUCE GROUSE						
Manitoba			2			Fig. 8
Totals	2		6	6		

TABLE 15

Relationship of major peaks in colored fox, mink, marten, and fisher to lynx peaks at the continental level[1]

Lynx	Colored fox	Mink	Marten	Fisher
1838	– –	– –	1836	– –
1847	– –	– –	1846	– –
1857	1857	1856	1855	– –
1866	1866	1867	1864	– –
1876	1876	1876	1873	– –
1886	1886	1883	1884	– –
1895	1895	1895	1893	– –
1905	1905	– –	– –	– –
1925	1925	1923	– –	1927
1935	1935	1933	– –	1936
1944	1943	1941	– –	?
1954	– –	– –	– –	1954
Av. no. yr. before or after lynx	+0.1	+1.3	+2.0	−1.0

[1] Data prior to 1905 taken from Hewitt (1921) and corrected to biological year or year of production according to Elton and Nicholson (1942b). Lynx and fisher peaks after 1905 interpreted from Dominion Bureau of Statistics records; colored fox and mink peaks taken from Butler (1953).

TABLE 16

Amplitude of cycles, and peak densities as shown by censuses and indices of local snowshoe hare and ruffed grouse populations

State or province	Locality	Time of year	Av. ratio of numbers during peak year to those during subsequent low	No. of sets of peaks and lows involved	Densities during peak year (no./sq. mi.)	Approx. lat.	Sources of reference data
			SNOWSHOE HARE				
Alberta	Anzac	May-Apr.	183:1	1	--	56°	Keith (pers. files)
Ontario	Oba	winter	17:1	1	--	50°	Hess (1946)
Minnesota	Cloquet Forest	Apr.-May	75:1	1	149	47°	Marshall (1954, and in litt.)
Wisconsin	Bayfield County	Nov.	13:1	1	--	47°	Buss and Buss (1947)
Minnesota	Lake Alexander	Feb. summer	15:1	1	478, 160 1049	46°	Green and Evans (1940); Chitty and Nicholson (1943)
Ontario	Frank's Bay	?	--	--	1200	46°	MacLulich (1937)
	Algonquin Park	?	--	--	300	46°	
	Buckshot Lake	summer				45°	
	(swamps)		110:1	1	3300		
	(other)		3200:0	1	3200		
	(total)		2250:1	1	3400		
West Va.	Pocahontas County	summer-fall	14:1	2	--	38°	Brooks (1955, and in litt.)
			RUFFED GROUSE				
Manitoba	Aweme	spring	13:1	2	--	50°	Criddle (1930)
North Dakota	Turtle Mts.	spring	4:1	1	--	49°	Johnson (1958)
	Pembina Hills	spring	3:1	1	--	49°	
Minnesota	Cloquet Forest	Oct.	13:1	1	353	47°	King (1937)
		April	>5:1	2	160, 49, 83		Marshall (1954, and in litt.)
Wisconsin	Bayfield County	Nov.	9:1	1	--	47°	Buss and Buss (1947)
	Ladysmith	Jan.-Dec.	>3:1	1	--	45°	Grange (1936)
		spring	(15:1)	1	(278)		
Michigan	Pigeon River II	Sept.	5:1	1	123	45°	G. A. Ammann (in litt.)
	Houghton Lake	Sept.	15:1	1	134	44°	
	Rifle River	fall	4:1	1	180	44°	Palmer (1956)
	Gladwin Refuge	fall	10:1	1	159	44°	

TABLE 17

Amplitude of grouse and snowshoe hare cycles in state and provincial hunting-kill data[1]

State or province	Period	Ptarmigan	Ruffed grouse	Prairie grouse	Spruce grouse	Snowshoe[2] hare	Sources of reference data
		Ratios of hunting kill per license — major peaks *vs.* subsequent lows — showing mean ratio and range of ratios					
Alaska	1925–52	*5.6:1(2)[3] 6.7–4.5				*9.8:1(3) 23–3.0	Buckley (1954)
British Columbia	1950–58		2.2:1(1)	3.5:1(1)			Figs. 3, 7
Alberta	1950–56		*4.6:1(1)	2.8:1(1)			Figs. 3, 7
Saskatchewan	1950–58		2.5:1(1)	2.0:1(1)			Figs. 3, 7
Manitoba	1932–58[4]		*17:1(3) 34–7.0	*8.6:1(3) 15–4.2	*16:1(2) 17–16		Figs. 3, 7
Minnesota	1939–58[5]		*3.3:1(2) 4.7–1.8	2.8:1(1)		*3.1:1(2) 3.8–2.3	Figs. 2, 6, 11
Wisconsin	1931–58		*3.8:1(3) 5.7–2.4	*5.7:1(2) 6.7–4.7		8.2:1(3) 12–5.9	Figs. 2, 6, 11
Michigan	1937–58[6]		2.8:1(2) 3.0–2.5	*3.2:1(2) 4.4–2.0		3.4:1(2) 4.0–2.8	Figs. 2, 6, 11
Average			6.5:1	4.6:1		6.7:1	

[1] Where an asterisk (*) precedes a ratio, the ratio is probably minimal; closed seasons during lows in Alaska, Manitoba, Wisconsin, and Michigan necessitated the use of the lowest kill figure — either preceding or following the closed season. In other instances the peak kill was in doubt.

[2] Alaska data include arctic hares.

[3] Number of sets of peaks and lows involved.

[4] Spruce grouse kill estimates cover period 1935–58, ratios computed from Tables D and I.

[5] Prairie grouse kill estimates cover period 1948–58, snowshoe hare 1942–58.

[6] Prairie grouse kill estimates cover period 1937–54.

TABLE 18

Amplitude of snowshoe hare and lynx cycles in regional
Hudson's Bay Company fur returns[1]

| Region | Period | Ratios of fur takes during major peaks to those during subsequent lows, showing mean ratio and range of ratios | |
		Snowshoe hare	Lynx
Hudson Bay	1849–	242:1(5)[2]	
Drainage	1904	960–6.3	
H.B.C. Districts			
Mackenzie	1821–		39:1(11)
River	1934		114–7.4
Athabasca	1821–		222:1(7)
Basin	91		1091–15
North	1821–		32:1(7)
Central	91		79–6.5
West	1821–		53:1(7)
Central	91		125–9.1
Upper	1821–		75:1(7)
Saskatchewan	91		170–17
Winnipeg	1821–		18:1(7)
Basin	91		34–5.8
Average			70:1

[1] References: MacLulich (1957), Elton and Nicholson (1942b).
[2] Number of sets of peaks and lows involved.

TABLE 19

Amplitude of cycles in the provincial and territorial fur returns of various species [1]

Province or territory	Period		Ratios of fur takes during major peaks to those during subsequent lows, showing mean ratio and range of ratios				
		Lynx	Colored fox	Coyote	Fisher	Mink	Muskrat
Northwest Territories	1919–57	5.0:1(4)[2] 5.9–2.9					
British Columbia	1919–57	4.9:1(3) 65–3.3	4.9:1(2) 5.5–4.9				
Alberta	1919–57	7.9:1(3) 13.4–3.4	10.4:1(2) 10.7–10.1	3.8:1(2) 5.4–2.1			
Saskatchewan	1919–57	4.1:1(2) 5.4–2.8	5.2:1(3) 7.7–3.8	4.1:1(3) 7.2–1.7			
Manitoba	1919–57[3]	5.0:1(3) 8.1–2.2	4.4:1(2) 4.7–4.0	5.3:1(2) 6.4–4.1	18:1(3) 44–4.7	1.9:1(3) 2.4–1.6	2.2:1(3) 2.6–1.7
Ontario	1919–57	4.8:1(4) 6.1–2.7	3.1:1(2) 3.8–2.4				
Quebec	1919–57	6.9:1(4) 14–1.3					
Nova Scotia	1919–57		3.6:1(2) 5.4–1.7				
Average		5.6:1	5.2:1	4.3:1			

[1] Ratios computed from data given in Tables L, M, N, O, P, Q.

[2] Number of sets of peaks and lows involved.

[3] Fur returns for mink and muskrat cover period 1924–57.

TABLE 20

Amplitude of cycles in the contintental fur returns of various species

Area	Period	Lynx	Colored fox	Coyote	Marten	Mink	Sources of reference data
			Ratios of fur takes during major peaks to those during subsequent lows, showing mean ratio and range of ratios				
Canada	1821–1911	13:1(9)[1] 31–8.0					Hewitt (1921)
Canada	1850–1913		3.4:1(6) 4.7–1.5				Hewitt (1921)
Canada	1835–80				2.6:1(5) 2.9–2.3		Hewitt (1921)
Northern Dept. H.B.C.	1821–91	20:1(7) 34–7.7					Elton and Nicholson (1942b)
Canada	1919–57	3.7:1(3) 4.4–3.3					Fig. 23
Canada	1919–50		2.6:1(2) 3.3–1.9			3.2:1(3) 4.0–2.5	Fig. 23
Prairie Provinces	1919–57		4.9:1(2) 5.3–4.4	3.3:1(2) 4.5–2.0			Fig. 23

[1] Number of sets of peaks and lows involved.

TABLE 21

Subjective estimates of snowshoe hare populations during peak years, and related observations

State or province	Locality	Year and time of year	Estimated density during peak years (no./sq. mi.) or other remarks	References
Alberta	McMurray	1949 Dec.	3,000–6,000 on limited tracts	Rowan (1950b)
	Athabasca	1952 Nov.	30,000 on favorable sites	Rowan (1954, and pers. comm.)
Manitoba	Carberry	1886 fall	5,000	Seton (1909)
	Aweme	1922 & 1933	3,000–3,500	Criddle (1938)
	Riding Mt. Natl. Park	1932–33 winter	4,500–5,000	MacLulich (1937) quoting H. U. Green *in litt.*
	White-mouth	1933 fall	20,000	MacLulich (1937) quoting V. B. Latta *in litt.*
Wisconsin	Sarona	?	1,000	Bailey (1946)
New York	Valcour Island	1943 fall	700 over whole island, 1,000 in habitable hare cover	Cook and Robeson (1945)
Alberta	Rocky Mt. House	1942–43 winter	1,700 snowshoe hares taken off of ½ section	Rowan (1950b) quoting H. Stelfox *in litt.*
	Athabasca	1952 Nov.	145 snowshoe hares counted at dusk along 1 mi. of road	Keith (pers. files)
British Columbia	Quesnel	1933	140 snowshoe hares seen along 4 mi. road	Cowan (1938)
Ontario	Kapus-kasing	1933 Dec. 9 & 16	55 snowshoe hares shot off of 40 ac.	MacLulich (1937) quoting J. Raeburn *in litt.*
	Nipissing	1932–33 winter	1,000 snowshoe hares taken off of 4 sq. mi.	MacLulich (1937) quoting J. Anderson *in litt.*
Minnesota	Cloquet Forest	?	200 snowshoe hares killed on 80 ac. in one day	Leopold (1931)
		1923? fall	20–50 snowshoe hares counted per mi. of road; 176 per mi. along railroad	Leopold (1931)
Michigan	Higgins Lake	?	157 snowshoe hares killed in one season on 20 ac.	Leopold (1931)

TABLE 22

Relationship of snowshoe hare litter size to latitude

Region	Period	Av. litter size [1]	Approximate latitude	References
Alaska	1937	4.91 ± 0.32(44)	60°–66°	Philip (1939)
Alberta	1949–52, 1956–57	3.83 ± 0.25(96)	56°	Keith (pers. files)
Manitoba	1933	4.08 ± 0.43(26)	51°	MacLulich (1937)
Manitoba	1923–35	3.44 ± 0.21(149)	50°	Criddle (1938)
Ontario	1933, 1935	2.46 ± 0.36(26)	49°	MacLulich (1937)
Minnesota	1931–35	2.82 ± 0.10(266)	46°	Aldous (1937)
Minnesota	1932–38	2.90 ± ? (140)	46°	Green and Evans (1940)
Minnesota	1932–35	*2.42 ± 0.30(36)	46°	Aldous (1937)
Maine	1939–40	*2.88 ± 0.22(81)	45°	Severaid (1942)
Maine	1941	*2.96 ± ? (80)	45°	Severaid (1942)
New York	1941–43	*2.40 ± ? (68)	43°	Smith (1950)

[1] Where preceded by an asterisk (*) values refer to actual litter sizes, for the most part born in captivity. Other values refer to embryo counts made during postmortems. Confidence limits are at 95 percent level, and sample sizes are shown in brackets.

TABLE 23

Some observations and comments on the time of the "die-off" among snowshoe hare populations

State, province or territory	Locality	Years of decline	Months or seasons of decline	Summary of observers' comments	References
Alberta	Dunvegan	1848	winter	Hares found dead in their forms on repeated occasions, apparently diseased.	Clarke (1942) quoting B. R. Ross
Ontario- Manitoba	Lake of the Woods– Winnipeg River	1857	spring- summer	Large numbers of hares found dead in the woods.	Hind (1860)
Northwest Territories	Upper Mackenzie	1904	Jan. and Feb.	"many thousands of rabbits perished from disease"	Preble (1908)
Alberta	Pembina River	1907	spring	"In the spring of 1907 the hares died off"	Henderson (1923)
Minnesota	Red Lake	1912	late winter	Dead and sick or weak rabbits observed by rangers	Cox (1936)
Northwest Territories	Mackenzie Delta	1914	early spring	"rabbits were from time to time found dead in large numbers on the west branch of the Mackenzie."	Anderson (1937)
Manitoba	Aweme	1923	April- May?	"disease . . . reduced the rabbits from almost the peak of their abundance to great scarcity in a few months."	Criddle (1938)
Alaska	Copper, Nizina, and lower Chitina rivers	1924– 25	winter	Counted as many as 14 dead rabbits per mile of railroad; estimated up to 1,200 dead per square mile in spring of 1925; had died in white winter pellage.	Laing *et al.* (1929)

TABLE 23 continued

State, province or territory	Locality	Years of decline	Months or seasons of decline	Summary of observers' comments	References
Northwest Territories	Mackenzie Delta	1933	coldest part of winter	"dead rabbits were found occasionally. These animals were always in poor condition, but showed no sign of disease and, in my opinion, had frozen or starved to death."	Porsild (1945)
New York	Valcour Island	1943–44	winter	Population decreased drastically from fall of 1943. In spring of 1944, 112 hare remains found — predation indicated in only 17 cases.	Crissey and Darrow (1949)
Northwest Territories	Mackenzie Delta	1946	winter– early summer?	Hares crashed after peak in winter of 1945–46; though still very common in July 1946. Three carcasses found but had no significant external lesions.	Banfield (1951)
Alberta	Athabasca	1952–53	winter	Noticeable decrease between early November and late December; greatest decrease from January to April.	Keith (pers. files)

Map A. — Northern North America showing provinces and states referred to in text. Settlements, study areas and other localities mentioned are numbered; the key to these numbers is given below and on the facing page.

Alaska
1 Copper, Nizina, and lower Chitina rivers
2 Tanana Valley

Alberta
1 Anzac
2 Athabasca
3 Chip Lake
4 Dunvegan
5 Edmonton
6 Jasper National Park
7 McMurray
8 Pembina River
9 Rocky Mountain House
10 Westlock
11 Whitecourt
12 Wood Buffalo National Park

British Columbia
1 Atlin
2 Quesnel

California
1 Sage Hen Creek

Indiana
1 Morocco

Manitoba
1 Aweme, Carberry, and Treesbank
2 Island Lake
3 Riding Mountain National Park
4 Whitemouth
5 York Factory

Michigan
1 Beaver Island
2 Bullock Ranch, and Seney National Wildlife Refuge
3 Drummond Island, and Munuscong State Park
4 Fletcher, Higgins Lake, and Houghton Lake
5 Gladwin Refuge, and Rifle River
6 Pigeon River

Minnesota
1 Cloquet
2 Kelliher, and Red Lake
3 Lake Alexander

Montana
1 Bull Island

New Jersey
1 Wyanokie

New York
1 Adirondack Area, Hale Brook Park, and Valcour Island
2 Connecticut Hill

North Carolina
1 Yancy County

North Dakota
1 Pembina Hills
2 Turtle Mountains

Northwest Territories
1 Artillery Lake
2 Eskimo Lake
3 Eskimo Point
4 Fort Resolution
5 Tuktoyaktuk

Ontario
1 Algonquin Provincial Park, Nipissing District, and Bigger Lake
2 Buckshot Lake
3 Chapleau, and Gogama
4 Fort Moose
5 Frank's Bay
6 Kapuskasing, Smoky Falls, and Oba
7 Lake of the Woods
8 Toronto

Pennsylvania
1 Hawk Mountain

Quebec
1 Eastmain (East Main)

Saskatchewan
1 Cumberland House
2 Emma Lake
3 Moose Jaw
4 Prince Albert
5 Prince Albert National Park
6 Qu'Appelle Valley
7 Yorkton

Washington
1 Pullman

West Virginia
1 Gaudineer Knob, and Pocahontas
  County

Wisconsin
1 Bayfield County
2 Cedar Grove
3 Cedar Rapids, Ladysmith, Otter
  Creek, and Sarona
4 Faville Grove
5 Plainfield

Yukon
1 Macmillan Region

Map B. — Northern North America showing the approximate position of former Hudson's Bay Company fur districts (after Elton and Nicholson, 1942b), the approximate limit of the northern coniferous forest and its ecotones, and certain geographical features mentioned in text.

TABLE A

Ruffed grouse population indices on small areas for seven or more years

Year	Grouse nests in a 26-ac. wood— Aweme, Man. (spring)[1]	Av. No. grouse seen per day grouse seen— Ladysmith, Wis. (Jan.-Dec.)[2]	Grouse per sq. mi. — Cloquet, Minn. (April)[3]	Grouse per sq. mi. — Pigeon River, Area II, Mich. (Sept.)[4]	Grouse per sq. mi. — Houghton Lake, Mich. (Sept.)[4]	Grouse seen per hunter day — Bayfield County, Wis. (Nov.)[5]
1914	2					
1915	13					
1916	9					
1917	3					
1918	1					
1919	2					
1920	2	4.5				
1921	9	5.7				
1922	7	8.7				
1923	12	7.5				
1924	12	5.7				
1925	11	4.7				
1926	3	3.2				
1927	2	lower	15			
1928	1	3.0	23			
1929	1		37			
1930			61			
1931			96			
1932			139	123	81	
1933			160	110	134	
1934			160	59	51	
1935			55	23	58	
1936			24	53	9	
1937				64	17	
1938				90	37	
1939						
1940			34			5.3
1941			48			7.4
1942			49			3.9
1943			37			2.1
1944			20			1.0
1945			14			0.8
1946			lower			1.4
1947			25			
1948			47			
1949			65			
1950			83			
1951			85			

(Continued on page 148)

TABLE A *continued*

Year	Grouse nests in a 26-ac. wood— Aweme, Man. (spring)[1]	Av. No. grouse seen per day grouse seen — Ladysmith, Wis. (Jan.-Dec.)[2]	Grouse per sq. mi. — Cloquet, Minn. (April)[3]	Grouse per sq. mi. — Pigeon River, Area II, Mich. (Sept.)[4]	Grouse per sq. mi. — Houghton Lake, Mich. (Sept.)[4]	Grouse seen per hunter day — Bayfield County, Wis. (Nov.)[5]
1952			42			
1953			34			
1954			11			
1955			17			
1956			21			

[1] Criddle (1930).

[2] Grange (1936).

[3] Marshall (1954; and *in litt.*)

[4] G. A. Ammann (*in litt.*), Game Division, Michigan State Conservation Department.

[5] Buss and Buss (1947).

TABLE B
Snowshoe hare population indices on small areas for seven or more years

Year	Hares per sq. mi.— Lake Alexander, Minn. (Feb.)[1]	Hares taken on trap line— Oba, Ont. (winter)[2]	Hares seen per hunter day— Bayfield County, Wis. (Nov.)[3]	Hare pellets in plots— Pocahontas County, W. Va. (summer-fall)[4]	Hares per sq. mi.— Cloquet, Minn. (Apr.-May)[5]	Hares collected on study area— Anzac, Alta. (May-Apr.)[6]
1932	275	271				
1933	478	213				
1934	374	584				
1935	356	505				
1936	246	209				
1937	151	145				
1938	32	90				
1939	73	40				
1940	74	34	0.15			
1941	160	64	0.67			
1942	72	109	0.78	440		
1943		201	0.25	184		
1944		188	0.17	171		
1945			0.06	70		
1946			0.28	32	4	
1947				53	14	
1948				40	20	
1949				84	112	
1950				244	149	220
1951				570	90	366
1952				555	54	109
1953				544	48	62
1954				368	14	2
1955				149	2	5
1956				51		18
1957				41	6	43
1958				110	12	
1959				196	26	

[1] Green and Evans (1940), and Chitty and Nicholson (1943).
[2] Hess (1946); year refers to latter half of winter, e.g., 1932 refers to winter of 1931–32.
[3] Buss and Buss (1947).
[4] Brooks (1955, and *in litt.*).
[5] Marshall (1954, and *in litt.*).
[6] Keith (pers. files); year refers to latter half of winter.

TABLE C
Hunting license sales for nine states [1]

Year	North Dakota[2]	Michigan[3]	Wisconsin[4]	Minnesota[5]	Maine[6]	New York[7]	Pennsylvania[8]	Connecticut[9]	North Carolina[10]
1915							262,887		
1916							291,084		
1917							316,062		
1918							311,768		
1919							402,258		
1920							433,965		
1921							464,132		
1922							475,861		
1923							499,544	35,084	
1924							504,130	35,048	
1925							525,045	35,087	
1926							524,042	35,226	
1927							506,501	38,704	
1928							438,917	37,917	
1929							509,926	37,250	
1930							536,401	31,414	
1931			175,294				581,746	31,257	
1932			207,370			460,342	542,703	27,833	
1933			185,095			445,768	529,303	28,747	
1934			223,697			457,507	574,690	28,022	
1935			198,131			467,957	614,929	28,164	
1936			242,315			485,338	541,697	28,372	
1937		490,060	237,198			503,814	606,618	31,444	
1938	24,000	518,906	270,585			537,417	661,730	31,317	
1939	36,900	540,898	292,626	241,483		535,809	662,901	- -	
1940	39,586	540,564	298,529	286,993		413,468	679,168	35,275	
1941	55,080	616,432	328,802	295,473		429,715	686,356	41,043	
1942	54,603	576,694	312,501	270,660		404,766	649,215	43,309	
1943	41,322	512,204	292,348	225,309		342,430	582,734	38,000	
1944	58,951	554,175	286,570	231,145		352,099	607,900	40,402	
1945	66,894	556,206	290,785	234,142		381,912	713,621	43,972	
1946	70,029	691,591	380,115	322,290		517,009	856,020	56,112	
1947	61,980	540,989	378,041	183,904		476,474	850,435	56,192	
1948	73,927	587,134	418,419	324,644	156,000	504,991	882,925	50,119	
1949	73,176	628,764	455,680	334,296	158,000	454,396	839,947	50,049	286,259
1950	58,965	634,906	475,803	332,000	162,182	450,416	834,172	49,764	289,659
1951	66,102	644,589	369,747	327,611	164,968	469,545	857,322	51,377	303,031
1952	67,858	671,828	384,059	360,313	160,946		862,821	55,142	318,887
1953	49,641	724,358	396,944	314,194	171,022		890,447	57,396	341,399
1954	62,346	723,971	375,103	308,871	172,849		900,113	58,927	

TABLE C continued

Year	North Dakota[2]	Michi- gan[3]	Wiscon- sin[4]	Minne- sota[5]	Maine[6]	New York[7]	Pennsyl- vania[8]	Connec- ticut[9]	North Carolina[10]
1955	69,848	749,769	392,857	343,336	171,863		931,013	58,293	
1956	69,517	758,086	413,582	347,328	172,018		938,064		
1957	71,792	691,072	383,452	319,654	177,608		960,008		
1958	76,069	700,710	384,819	379,667	176,848				

[1] License-sale figures for North Dakota, Michigan, Wisconsin, Minnesota, and New York refer to "Small Game Licenses" which include upland game birds and waterfowl. Maine, Pennsylvania, Connecticut, and North Carolina figures are for total hunting-license sales.

[2] Obtained from A. T. Klett (*in litt.*), North Dakota Fish and Game Department.

[3] Taken from *History of License Sales* (2 pp. mimeo.) compiled by the Michigan Department of Conservation.

[4] Taken from *Wisconsin Game Kill and License Sales Charts*, issued yearly by the Wisconsin Conservation Department.

[5] Figures for 1939–52 taken from Erickson and Burcalow (1953); remainder obtained from the Minnesota Department of Conservation.

[6] Obtained from W. R. Degarmo (*in litt.*), Game Division, Maine Department of Inland Fisheries and Game.

[7] Obtained from J. Dell (*in litt.*), Division of Fish and Game, New York State Conservation Department.

[8] Taken from *Pennsylvania's Hunting Is a Big Business*, issued by the Pennsylvania Game Commission.

[9] Figures for 1923–47 taken from Sondrini (1950); remainder obtained from the Connecticut State Board of Fisheries and Game.

[10] Taken from *Biennial Reports* of the North Carolina Wildlife Resources Commission.

TABLE D
Hunting license sales for five Canadian provinces [1]

Year	British Columbia [2]	Alberta [3]	Saskatchewan [4]	Manitoba [5]	New Brunswick [6]
1930					3,943
1931					4,880
1932				8,550	4,463
1933				8,588	3,460
1934				6,988	2,715
1935				6,353	3,094
1936				7,018	3,457
1937				6,706	4,614
1938				7,565	5,319
1939				7,667	5,248
1940				7,449	4,135
1941				8,017	4,676
1942				9,536	5,045
1943				7,662	2,771
1944				8,224	2,921
1945				12,223	4,366
1946				12,465	5,498
1947				14,077	6,046
1948				15,112	6,564
1949				17,995	7,664
1950	67,000	37,247	33,927	18,927	7,096
1951	76,000	39,926	43,306	22,399	5,700
1952	76,000	51,825	51,607	25,283	6,036
1953	78,000	59,110	51,708	26,143	5,748
1954	81,000	60,161	52,672	24,940	5,603
1955	83,000	64,479	54,951	26,943	6,194
1956	89,000	73,972	57,898	30,880	6,847
1957	96,000		57,797	33,371	7,168
1958	105,000		56,657	34,492	6,854

[1] License-sale figures for Alberta, Saskatchewan, and Manitoba represent total "Game-Bird" licenses sold each year. In British Columbia a general hunting license is issued which is good for both game birds and big game. New Brunswick figures refer to "Game-Bird" license sales: a combined "Deer-Game-Bird" license is also issued.

[2] Obtained from J. Hatter (*in litt.*), Fish and Game Branch, British Columbia Department of Recreation and Conservation.

[3] Taken from *Annual Reports* of the Alberta Department of Lands and Forests.

[4] Taken from the 1957–58 and 1958–59 *Annual Reports* of the Saskatchewan Department of Natural Resources.

[5] Taken from *Annual Reports* of the Manitoba Department of Mines and Natural Resources.

[6] Obtained from H. Haswell (*in litt.*), Fish and Wildlife Branch, New Brunswick Department of Lands and Mines.

TABLE E
Ruffed grouse hunting-kill estimates for eight states

Year	Michigan[1]	Wisconsin[2]	Minnesota[3]	Maine[4]	New York[5]	Pennsylvania[6]	Connecticut[7]	North Carolina[8]
1915						186,344		
1916						126,274		
1917						112,287		
1918						C.S.		
1919						287,001		
1920						425,000		
1921						325,000		
1922						600,000		
1923						580,440	62,213	
1924						330,000	25,585	
1925						355,980	30,992	
1926						298,196	34,037	
1927						325,529	24,510	
1928						150,000	9,562	
1929						C.S.	C.S.	
1930						83,787	19,788	
1931		56,383				170,369	23,184	
1932		317,007			55,845	134,135	19,594	
1933		318,410			68,940	164,285	24,563	
1934		131,762			84,614	135,480	23,785	
1935		72,778			128,301	190,955	42,157	
1936		C.S.[9]			80,282	96,909	20,581	
1937	237,156	C.S.			73,558	177,683	21,061	
1938	316,787	80,664			140,851	224,479	22,552	
1939	296,676	144,002	95,218		157,151	237,245	– –	
1940	289,961	246,804	218,000		170,135	221,474	20,675	
1941	349,631	353,461	384,000		150,533	187,990	19,517	
1942	381,602	421,728	361,500		130,926	237,408	22,103	
1943	290,117	354,448	171,178		61,888	117,219	13,846	
1944	260,475	115,389	C.S.		57,758	101,224	11,842	
1945	165,475	C.S.	C.S.		42,667	46,412	8,453	
1946	182,642	C.S.	C.S.		40,019	C.S.	10,780	
1947	228,858	C.S.	C.S.	100,000	40,797	29,922	11,537	
1948	354,250	249,221	353,840	105,000	45,160	24,297	8,694	
1949	570,641	736,693	885,309	100,500	48,332	36,304	11,449	9,169
1950	479,665	798,932	936,351	170,400	76,295	36,403	9,330	16,736
1951	630,588	735,820	1,420,325	155,645	85,530	45,250	14,305	25,612
1952	807,406	760,246	1,246,563	152,450		67,357	14,203	21,803
1953	700,489	814,351	711,255	162,015		62,028	11,302	17,181
1954	395,382 (393,810)[10]	321,722	368,414	135,375		53,643	10,082	

(Continued on page 154)

TABLE E continued

Year	Michigan[1]	Wisconsin[2]	Minnesota[3]	Maine[4]	New York[5]	Pennsylvania[6]	Connecticut[7]	North Carolina[8]
1955	(314,010)	365,656	424,431	185,690		64,185	8,526	
1956	(300,140)	645,191	329,702	194,900		49,847		
1957	(352,460)	546,765	409,000	232,375		41,694		
		(468,700)						
1958	(368,260)	(431,500)	510,288	151,670				

[1] Obtained from L. L. Eberhardt (*in litt.*), Michigan Department of Conservation.

[2] Taken from *Wisconsin Game Kill and License Sales Charts*, issued yearly by the Wisconsin Conservation Department.

[3] Figures for 1939–52 taken from Erickson and Burcalow (1953); remainder obtained from the Minnesota Department of Conservation.

[4] Obtained from W. R. DeGarmo (*in litt.*), Game Division, Maine Department of Inland Fisheries and Game.

[5] Obtained from J. Dell (*in litt.*), Division of Fish and Game, New York State Conservation Department.

[6] Taken from *Pennsylvania's Hunting Is a Big Business*, issued by the Pennsylvania Game Commission.

[7] Figures for 1923–47 taken from Sondrini (1950); remainder obtained from the Connecticut State Board of Fisheries and Game.

[8] Taken from Barick and Critcher (1956).

[9] Closed season.

[10] Kill estimates based on new sampling procedures.

TABLE F
Ruffed grouse hunting-kill estimates for five Canadian provinces

Year	British Columbia[1]	Alberta[2]	Saskatchewan[3]	Manitoba[4]	New Brunswick[5]
1930					37,647
1931					44,469
1932				18,071	39,423
1933				21,702	60,563
1934				15,051	31,713
1935				2,336	39,272
1936				1,747	33,225
1937				2,560	73,700
1938				5,717	92,733
1939				5,384	76,728
1940				6,855	35,065
1941				8,448	45,245
1942				9,749	61,820
1943				2,596	32,000
1944				C.S.[6]	33,000
1945				C.S.	57,000
1946				C.S.	60,732
1947				C.S.	68,045
1948				C.S.	73,010
1949				2,879	42,780
1950	106,800	69,730	6,603	2,851	81,780
1951	142,900	72,000	26,372	15,453	64,115
1952	177,200	85,710	55,294	12,615	65,615
1953	186,000	44,130	43,418	3,454	67,185
1954	107,000	25,100	25,501	1,259	66,879
1955	90,500	36,000	30,995	C.S.	58,124
1956	98,100	36,900	25,141	645	56,670
1957	161,300		44,627	3,492	71,323
1958	315,100		43,175	7,025	77,590

[1] Obtained from J. Hatter (*in litt.*), Fish and Game Branch, British Columbia Department of Recreation and Conservation.

[2] Figures for 1951 and 1956 obtained from G. Mitchell (*in litt.*), Game Branch, Alberta Department of Lands and Forests; remainder from *Annual Reports* of the Alberta Department of Lands and Forests.

[3] Taken from the 1957–58 and 1958–59 *Annual Reports* of the Saskatchewan Department of Natural Resources.

[4] Obtained from E. F. Bossenmaier (*in litt.*), Game Branch, Manitoba Department of Mines and Natural Resources.

[5] Obtained from H. Haswell (*in litt.*), Fish and Wildlife Branch, New Brunswick Department of Lands and Mines; data include some spruce grouse.

[6] Closed season.

TABLE G

Prairie grouse hunting-kill estimates for four states

Year	Combined sharp-tailed and pinnated grouse		Sharp-tailed grouse	
	Michigan[1]	Wisconsin[2]	Minnesota[3]	North Dakota[4]
1931		52,857		
1932		123,012		
1933		140,091		
1934		72,039		
1935		33,476		
1936		C.S.[5]		
1937	30,624	C.S.		
1938	37,040	44,612		71,000
1939	39,664	75,519		127,000
1940	38,855	77,872		133,000
1941	36,682	72,837		150,000
1942	39,430	77,209		144,000
1943	25,969	C.S.		110,000
1944	17,879	C.S.		110,000
1945	15,049	C.S.		70,000
1946	11,785	C.S.		C.S.
1947	14,683	C.S.		10,000
1948	23,716	C.S.	13,687	130,000
1949	34,038	C.S.	153,637	50,000
1950	33,588	66,851	82,726	50,000
1951	32,684	62,078	97,832	70,000
1952	26,824	40,457	116,198	96,000
1953	23,856	28,765	74,392	70,000
1954	19,547	9,499	60,233	75,000
1955		12,928	61,965	91,000
1956		10,230	40,473	166,000
1957		10,806	54,020	83,000
		(9,000)[6]		
1958		(5,900)	66,979	119,000

[1] Obtained from L. L. Eberhardt (*in litt.*), Michigan Department of Conservation.

[2] Taken from *Wisconsin Game Kill and License Sales Charts*, issued yearly by the Wisconsin Conservation Department.

[3] Figures for 1948–52 taken from Erickson and Burcalow (1953); remainder obtained from the Minnesota Department of Conservation.

[4] Obtained from A. T. Klett(*in litt.*), North Dakota Fish and Game Department.

[5] Closed season.

[6] Kill estimates based on new sampling procedures.

TABLE H

Prairie grouse hunting-kill estimates for four Canadian provinces

| Year | Sharp-tailed grouse | | | | Pinnated grouse (Manitoba) | Total prairie grouse (Manitoba) |
	British Columbia[1]	Alberta[2]	Saskatchewan[3]	Manitoba[4]		
1932						48,459
1933						47,468
1934						32,054
1935						8,930
1936						6,458
1937						8,474
1938						21,008
1939						20,262
1940						23,956
1941						25,429
1942						25,859
1943						8,765
						C.S.[5]
1948			19,335			C.S.
1949			43,587	2,122	1,882	4,004
1950	16,000	72,810	54,999	3,540	2,939	6,479
1951	16,200	67,000	82,880	9,446	8,265	17,711
1952	28,200	86,460	129,614	8,600	6,662	15,262
1953	16,000	57,000	121,515	6,583	C.S.	
1954	8,700	46,000	108,808	C.S.	C.S.	
1955	10,400	53,900	100,582	C.S.	C.S.	
1956	10,900	51,700	71,664	3,238	C.S.	
1957	15,100		110,696	7,901	C.S.	
1958	40,300		105,151	16,583	C.S.	

[1] Obtained from J. Hatter (*in litt.*), Fish and Game Branch, British Columbia Department of Recreation and Conservation.

[2] Figures for 1951 and 1956 obtained from G. Mitchell (*in litt.*), Game Branch, Alberta Department of Lands and Forests; remainder from *Annual Reports* of the Alberta Department of Lands and Forests.

[3] Taken from the 1957–58 and 1958–59 *Annual Reports* of the Saskatchewan Department of Natural Resources.

[4] Obtained from E. F. Bossenmaier (*in litt.*), Game Branch, Manitoba Department of Mines and Natural Resources.

[5] Closed season.

TABLE I

Blue and spruce grouse hunting-kill estimates for three Canadian provinces

Year	Blue grouse (British Columbia)[1]	Spruce grouse	
		Saskatchewan[2]	Manitoba[3]
1935			1,137
1936			717
1937			778
1938			2,067
1939			1,879
1940			2,422
1941			3,206
1942			3,714
1943			1,161
			C.S.[4]
1949			457
1950	100,400	C.S.	707
1951	69,300	C.S.	3,792
1952	113,000	8,779	3,502
1953	147,900	6,670	1,102
1954	107,000	4,270	630
1955	66,200	4,618	C.S.
1956	61,000	3,858	322
1957	89,400	4,914	C.S.
1958	128,800	9,634	1,999

[1] Obtained from J. Hatter (*in litt.*), Fish and Game Branch, British Columbia Department of Recreation and Conservation.

[2] Taken from the 1957–58 and 1958–59 *Annual Reports* of the Saskatchewan Department of Natural Resources.

[3] Obtained from E. F. Bossenmaier (*in litt.*), Game Branch, Manitoba Department of Mines and Natural Resources.

[4] Closed season.

TABLE J

Hungarian partridge hunting-kill estimates for three Canadian provinces

Year	Alberta[1]	Saskatchewan[2]	Manitoba[3]
1932			1,974
1933			3,466
1934			3,588
1935			2,118
1936			2,198
1937			2,057
1938			3,872
1939			6,375
1940			13,386
1941			18,241
1942			16,551
1943			4,834
			C.S.[4]
1949		483	54
1950	106,970	22,425	103
1951	92,000	92,788	1,844
1952	136,600	83,529	2,457
1953	140,500	97,190	1,226
1954	116,600	72,619	468
1955	134,900	65,517	– –
1956	77,400	42,166	174
1957		49,049	359
1958		47,445	1,222

[1] Figures for 1951 and 1956 obtained from G. Mitchell (*in litt.*), Game Branch, Alberta Department of Lands and Forests; remainder from *Annual Reports* of the Alberta Department of Lands and Forests.

[2] Taken from the 1957–58 and 1958–59 *Annual Reports* of the Saskatchewan Department of Natural Resources.

[3] Obtained from E. F. Bossenmaier (*in litt.*), Game Branch, Manitoba Department of Mines and Natural Resources.

[4] Closed season.

TABLE K

Snowshoe hare hunting-kill estimates for seven states

Year	Michigan[1]	Wisconsin[2]	Minnesota[3]	Maine[4]	New York[5]	Penn-sylvania[6]	Con-necticut[7]
1923							878
1924							758
1925							645
1926							858
1927							962
1928							703
1929							752
1930						20,602	1,109
1931		633,915				26,245	951
1932		631,007			42,255	19,890	917
1933		506,725			30,301	23,139	1,206
1934		320,804			20,071	17,995	673
1935		178,846			34,311	8,659	1,126
1936		152,736			14,024	C.S.	473
1937	294,164	60,081			16,010	2,420	1,056
1938	512,917	83,906			– –	2,120	688
1939	549,796	110,953			29,244	C.S.[8]	– –
1940	392,762	93,012			32,713	C.S.	1,316
1941	401,433	173,683			32,621	C.S.	1,363
1942	287,414	109,185	99,100		28,426	6,019	1,532
1943	244,657	124,081	53,805		21,364	3,716	1,001
1944	156,069	26,854	34,688		26,634	3,665	1,043
1945	254,837	27,567	22,283		21,004	736	591
1946	314,090	57,084	49,143		22,399	3,133	1,042
1947	235,354	64,489	29,263	120,000	26,196	5,518	1,204
1948	397,911	177,548	65,973	138,500	30,749	5,616	1,122
1949	495,465	310,132	81,516	123,000	32,124	5,948	1,061
1950	336,011	154,428	70,064	133,375	33,815	1,445	972
1951	395,655	137,525	105,598	98,630	32,018	1,506	1,111
1952	343,214	81,955	125,201	129,360		3,454	1,332
1953	299,651	75,922	75,591	179,675		4,237	859
1954	205,731 (351,820)[9]	40,573	73,681	174,000		2,736	1,137
1955	(284,540)	40,100	75,446	193,525		2,192	752
1956	(282,920)	72,254	61,152	211,000		1,969	
1957	(283,740)	117,325 (100,600)	48,150	304,600		1,614	
1958	(313,070)	(64,900)	60,135	202,380			

[1] Obtained from L. L. Eberhardt (*in litt.*), Michigan Department of Conservation.

[2] Taken from *Wisconsin Game Kill and License Sales Charts*, issued yearly by the Wisconsin Conservation Department.

[3] Obtained from the Minnesota Department of Conservation.

[4] Obtained from W. R. Degarmo (*in litt.*), Game Division, Maine Department of Inland Fisheries and Game.

TABLE K continued

[5] Obtained from J. Dell (*in litt.*), Division of Fish and Game, New York State Conservation Department.

[6] Taken from *Pennsylvania's Hunting Is a Big Business*, issued by the Pennsylvania Game Commission.

[7] Figures for 1923–47 taken from Sondrini (1950); remainder obtained from the Connecticut State Board of Fisheries and Game.

[8] Closed season.

[9] Kill estimates based on new sampling procedures.

TABLE L
Mink fur returns for Saskatchewan and Manitoba

Biological year	Saskatchewan[1]	Manitoba[2]	Biological year	Saskatchewan[1]	Manitoba[2]
1914	15,585		1936	6,577	15,083
1915	9,696		1937	3,871	11,021
1916	6,757		1938	4,659	13,894
1917	6,443		1939	6,749	17,676
1918	6,744		1940	12,469	26,382
1919	10,637		1941	8,579	28,712
1920	11,206		1942	6,839	18,356
1921	8,937		1943	9,990	21,067
1922	13,977		1944	6,561	15,338
1923	11,430		1945	5,831	12,801
1924	13,955	12,712	1946	8,088	15,850
1925	6,635	16,355	1947	9,579	18,778
1926	7,855	10,748	1948	10,672	22,932
1927	5,485	9,833	1949	16,195	29,456
1928	5,605	11,308	1950	12,596	25,212
1929	5,016	10,729	1951	12,833	26,056
1930	6,028	11,701	1952	18,853	26,401
1931	6,287	12,941	1953	11,493	18,432
1932	11,978	20,860	1954	14,613	17,579
1933	15,730	28,888	1955	18,514	15,384
1934	14,850	21,493	1956	38,298	27,041
1935	9,766	17,037	1957	50,237	37,854

[1] Taken from the 1957–58 and 1958–59 *Annual Reports* of the Saskatchewan Department of Natural Resources; reportedly refer only to wild-fur production.

[2] Obtained from E. F. Bossenmaier (*in litt.*), Game Branch, Manitoba Department of Mines and Natural Resources; reportedly refer only to wild-fur production.

TABLE M
Muskrat fur returns for three Canadian provinces and all of Canada

Biological year	Saskatchewan[1]	Manitoba[2]	Ontario[3]	Canada[4]
1914	656,917			
1915	925,898			
1916	820,720			
1917	719,805			
1918	1,157,455			
1919	890,066		505,296	2,377,424
1920	504,738		462,136	2,015,481
1921	267,497		616,890	3,060,526
1922	728,132		515,386	3,846,161
1923	1,352,870		638,899	2,985,395
1924	1,006,863	306,906	534,739	2,575,142
1925	856,829	441,623	387,022	1,953,545
1926	483,858	226,841	469,947	1,774,954
1927	389,436	213,866	514,376	1,963,118
1928	533,524	236,398	714,019	2,785,994
1929	431,865	251,986	643,999	2,109,232
1930	401,292	300,624	723,325	2,639,086
1931	361,523	441,378	640,390	2,601,660
1932	590,453	421,799	637,649	2,731,490
1933	686,062	385,060	522,493	2,538,565
1934	378,285	321,828	444,728	1,983,747
1935	197,979	271,885	359,294	1,630,231
1936	98,768	324,820	361,083	1,607,897
1937	46,699	285,440	471,203	1,748,239
1938	211,740	374,896	687,711	2,295,550
1939	584,736	682,375	737,098	3,241,089
1940	355,576	659,928	731,700	2,795,218
1941	107,091	331,362	617,503	2,408,436
1942	109,395	280,838	688,927	2,068,468
1943	114,481	581,862	638,568	2,038,868
1944	127,566	855,724	660,505	2,377,629
1945	417,501	958,099	824,924	3,420,496
1946	370,638	808,692	812,744	2,795,687
1947	510,730	822,998	862,490	3,569,157
1948	726,362	930,330	742,761	4,123,784
1949	473,212	796,456	562,587	3,138,609
1950	302,177	679,899	656,388	2,958,662
1951	542,170	599,794	741,814	3,292,110

TABLE M continued

Biological year	Saskatchewan[1]	Manitoba[2]	Ontario[3]	Canada[4]
1952	951,065	721,117	838,392	3,440,664
1953	678,470	790,472	780,090	3,362,495
1954	1,951,800	1,288,120	841,135	5,619,277
1955	1,731,978	1,462,472	500,111	4,518,731
1956	811,859	1,003,186	564,511	3,566,253
1957	600,752	680,891	446,578	

[1] Taken from the 1957–58 and 1958–59 *Annual Reports* of the Saskatchewan Department of Natural Resources.

[2] Obtained from E. F. Bossenmaier (*in litt.*), Game Branch, Manitoba Department of Mines and Natural Resources.

[3] Obtained from C. J. Ducharme (*in litt.*), Ontario Department of Lands and Forests, having been compiled from Dominion Bureau of Statistics data.

[4] Taken from *The Canada Yearbook*, issued annually by the Dominion Bureau of Statistics.

APPENDIX

TABLE N
Lynx fur returns for eight provinces or territories of Canada [1]

Biol. year	British Columbia	Alberta	Saskat- chewan	Manitoba	Ontario	Quebec	Northwest Territories	Yukon	Total
1919	730	1,045	991	1,295	1,176	2,440	367	334	8,378
1920	1,006	2,027	874	991	630	550	196	182	6,456
1921	2,103	3,620	1,451	1,847	805	689	476	626	11,617
1922	2,967	5,788	2,092	2,314	1,136	897	575	1,433	17,202
1923	4,881	7,374	1,614	4,939	2,154	1,593	1,300	2,526	26,381
1924	7,638	7,066	1,022	2,163	2,200	3,239	2,444	3,757	29,529
1925	4,667	7,662	1,382	2,399	3,884	4,978	4,552	3,503	33,027
1926	5,240	3,400	1,427	1,421	4,568	5,519	3,687	3,357	28,619
1927	3,559	2,851	588	744	3,845	2,889	3,101	3,786	21,363
1928	2,225	1,667	388	612	1,718	1,100	1,500	2,372	11,582
1929	1,564	1,109	541	629	871	646	776	1,436	7,572
1930	1,584	1,537	762	685	799	436	1,369	785	7,957
1931	1,599	1,517	695	749	1,088	399	1,664	699	8,410
1932	1,797	1,987	1,112	1,230	1,400	658	2,817	915	11,916
1933	2,285	2,112	1,757	1,992	2,138	1,078	4,395	1,024	16,781
1934	3,531	2,492	1,602	2,023	2,611	2,231	5,829	1,693	22,012
1935	3,551	2,300	1,232	1,342	2,608	4,081	4,391	2,943	22,448
1936	3,564	1,560	720	902	1,925	3,990	1,909	2,964	17,534
1937	1,752	822	616	671	1,014	1,915	981	2,752	10,523
1938	1,388	734	669	517	664	1,228	1,116	1,763	8,079
1939	1,070	1,028	782	426	491	795	1,628	1,191	7,411
1940	1,550	760	576	444	429	475	1,742	607	6,583
1941	1,135	772	582	654	546	919	1,626	745	6,979
1942	1,412	1,271	195	582	542	1,172	1,694	676	7,544
1943	2,625	1,474	340	525	687	1,819	1,803	891	10,164
1944	3,332	1,384	249	311	986	2,224	1,774	1,999	12,259
1945	1,271	553	127	149	768	2,922	1,701	1,815	9,306
1946	1,692	274	24	27	766	2,394	1,065	1,887	8,129
1947	1,610	110	361	20	616	1,571	1,070	1,190	6,548
1948	831	231	179	47	542	902	799	552	4,083
1949	515	366	363	200	479	828	332	631	3,714
1950	1,399	2,020	1,014	1,089	462	811	1,767	1,030	9,592
1951	870	813	1,017	1,170	215	765	1,637	166	6,653
1952	2,126	3,683	1,175	1,204	1,479	986	1,575	408	12,636
1953	1,517	2,965	848	911	1,769	1,068	1,244	554	10,876
1954	3,132	3,011	1,111	748	1,400	1,714	1,382	1,378	13,876
1955	2,239	1,184	574	645	918	1,469	602	2,029	9,660
1956	1,608	1,729	852	539	665	1,319	616	1,069	8,397
1957	1,569	654	1,567	1,547	1,083	1,515	617	406	8,958

[1] Obtained from the Dominion Bureau of Statistics.

TABLE O
Colored fox fur returns for seven Canadian provinces

Biological year	British Co- lumbia[1]	Alberta[2]	Saskatch- ewan[3]	Man- itoba[4]	Ontario[5]	New Bruns- wick[6]	Nova Scotia[1]	Prairie Provinces Total[7]
1914			8,145					
1915			9,718					
1916			9,962					
1917			5,279					
1918			3,132					
1919	461	477	1,962	3,742	10,649		2,077	6,181
1920	854	1,308	1,286	1,546	5,965		1,437	4,144
1921	1,311	2,449	1,461	2,943	16,828		1,387	6,853
1922	1,550	6,083	4,210	5,792	14,024		2,263	16,085
1923	2,153	11,511	5,567	13,334	18,643		3,116	29,412
1924	3,892	14,184	9,462	15,462	22,198	5,702	4,009	40,203
1925	3,766	11,835	10,557	15,276	30,874	5,410	3,023	34,481
1926	5,037	5,085	7,370	6,555	26,263	3,697	2,033	17,023
1927	2,286	1,330	5,383	4,958	26,039	2,978	1,280	9,049
1928	2,042	1,545	2,761	3,294	14,550	1,766	1,146	7,993
1929	921	1,474	3,154	4,393	11,076	2,039	739	8,179
1930	1,180	2,411	4,631	4,399	8,441	1,135	1,306	11,441
1931	1,071	4,047	6,869	7,259	9,564	953	2,525	18.175
1932	1,396	7,310	11,801	14,135	8,198	1,186	2,961	33,246
1933	2,548	13,395	17,477	26,232	13,995	1,235	2,723	57,104
1934	3,827	13,908	19,863	24,214	26,883	563	2,703	57,985
1935	4,593	7,616	8,093	12,695	38,545	2,060	2,377	28,404
1936	4,114	2,490	5,892	11,066	35,308	1,731	2,660	19,448
1937	1,603	1,371	5,515	11,166	23,502	1,493	1,830	17,052
1938	1,420	1,776	4,813	6,499	22,618	1,587	1,804	13,088
1939	1,056	3,105	6,075	7,166	18,267	1,504	1,666	16,346
1940	1,671	5,248	13,013	13,152	16,142	1,628	1,620	31,413
1941	2,390	14,789	21,280	29,658	32,038	1,070	2,914	65,727
1942	3,466	31,410	21,391	31,070	28,393	3,525	2,916	83,791
1943	7,912	31,645	25,935	30,603	59,892	3,338	3,700	88,183
1944	9,324	10,817	10,234	18,098	39,930	5,006	3,423	39,149
1945	4,395	6,226	4,072	12,781	45,688	4,009	3,649	23,079
1946	2,235	1,690	3,082	7,959	24,964	3,049	2,328	12,731
1947	873	556	2,133	4,200	16,459	2,230	1,318	6,889
1948	357	530	1,813	3,829	16,841	1,586	985	6,172
1949	252	622	1,908	2,614	9,206	1,559	871	5,144
1950	397	2,033	3,243	5,475	13,191	847	2,011	10,751
1951	181	1,054	2,333	2,252	10,027	610	1,632	5,639
1952	344	675	1,428	2,073	11,814	419	918	4,167
1953	141	741	1,272	1,557	5,424	495	565	3,549

(Continued on page 166)

TABLE O continued

Biological year	British Columbia[1]	Alberta[2]	Saskatch- ewan[3]	Man- itoba[4]	Ontario[5]	New Bruns- wick[6]	Nova Scotia[1]	Prairie Provinces Total[7]
1954	96	242	422	1,469	4,930	186	485	2,131
1955	59	50	354	1,236	2,619	237	590	1,639
1956	20	39	364	454	3,574	102	276	857
1957	788	165	880	1,385	2,031	273	640	2,429

[1] Obtained from J. H. Dickson (*in litt.*), Livestock and Animal Products Section, Agriculture Division, Dominion Bureau of Statistics, and may include ranch pelts prior to 1943. These data are for the red and cross color phases only.

[2] Returns for 1919–41, except 1921, taken from Rand (1948a) and apparently refer to wild-fur production; 1921 obtained from J. H. Dickson (*in litt.*), Livestock and Animal Products Section, Agriculture Division, Dominion Bureau of Statistics, and may include ranch pelts; 1942–57 taken directly from Alberta Game Branch files and refer to wild-fur production only. These data represent the red color phase only.

[3] Returns taken from the 1951–52 and 1958–59 *Annual Reports* of the Saskatchewan Department of Natural Resources, reportedly refer only to wild-fur production. Data here are for red, cross, black, and silver color phases.

[4] Returns for 1919–24 obtained from J. H. Dickson (*in litt.*), Livestock and Animal Products Section, Agriculture Division, Dominion Bureau of Statistics, and may include ranch pelts; 1925–57 obtained from E. F. Bossenmaier (*in litt.*), Game Branch, Manitoba Department of Mines and Natural Resources, reportedly refer only to wild-fur production. Data here are for red, cross, black, and silver color phases.

[5] Obtained from C. J. Ducharme (*in litt.*), Ontario Department of Lands and Forests, having been compiled from Dominion Bureau of Statistics data. These data apparently include all color phases.

[6] Obtained from H. Haswell (*in litt.*), New Brunswick Department of Lands and Mines, and indicate the number of animals on which a provincial royalty was collected. These data represent the red color phase only.

[7] Alberta, Saskatchewan, and Manitoba.

TABLE P

Coyote fur returns for the Prairie Provinces of Canada

Biological year	Alberta[1]	Saskatchewan[2]	Manitoba[3]	Total[4]
1914		2,266		
1915		13,355		
1916		33,666		
1917		37,064		
1918		25,859		
1919	8,881	21,551	20,845	51,277
1920	5,904	18,386	3,447	27,737
1921	13,483	5,182	4,474	23,139
1922	14,122	12,842	5,293	32,257
1923	32,315	12,490	6,517	51,322
1924	42,665	21,536	9,237	73,438
1925	56,639	31,009	8,053	95,701
1926	42,015	30,475	10,814	83,304
1927	20,150	29,926	13,056	63,132
1928	24,315	23,700	4,676	52,691
1929	14,871	12,704	2,653	30,228
1930	10,486	9,053	2,103	21,642
1931	10,999	9,693	2,031	22,723
1932	11,644	10,523	2,090	24,257
1933	15,556	12,528	3,655	31,739
1934	28,476	23,151	7,640	59,267
1935	27,541	20,103	5,942	53,586
1936	25,276	20,829	3,382	49,487
1937	19,464	17,707	2,424	39,595
1938	15,919	14,423	1,879	32,221
1939	15,259	13,799	1,996	31,054
1940	13,786	14,171	2,345	30,302
1941	18,763	18,900	4,023	41,686
1942	23,678	18,057	4,054	45,789
1943	31,028	26,785	7,745	65,558
1944	19,385	17,883	5,295	42,563
1945	13,669	19,994	3,801	37,464
1946	9,245	12,579	2,132	23,956
1947	10,512	8,823	2,268	21,603
1948	2,926	7,934	1,725	12,585
1949	5,152	8,860	1,677	15,689
1950	13,666	15,707	3,266	32,639
1951	4,902	6,153	1,726	12,781
1952	4,554	3,016	1,498	9,068
1953	2,685	769	888	4,342

(*Continued on page 168*)

APPENDIX

TABLE P continued

Biological year	Alberta[1]	Saskatchewan[2]	Manitoba[3]	Total[4]
1954	2,394	1,971	1,039	5,404
1955	1,680	1,907	951	4,538
1956	1,383	885	1,006	3,274
1957	1,705	838	1,243	3,786

[1] Returns for 1919–41, except 1921, taken from Rand (1948a); 1921 obtained from J. H. Dickson (*in litt.*), Livestock and Animal Products Section, Agriculture Division, Dominion Bureau of Statistics; 1942–57 taken directly from Alberta Game Branch files.

[2] Returns taken from the 1951–52 and 1958–59 *Annual Reports* of the Saskatchewan Department of Natural Resources.

[3] Returns for 1919–24 obtained from J. H. Dickson (*in litt.*), Livestock and Animal Products Section, Agriculture Division, Dominion Bureau of Statistics; 1925–27 obtained from E. F. Bossenmaier (*in litt.*), Game Branch, Manitoba Department of Mines and Natural Resources.

[4] Constitutes about 95 percent of Canadian total.

TABLE Q
Fisher fur returns from four Canadian provinces and all of Canada

Biological year	Manitoba[1]	Quebec[2]	Ontario[2]	British Columbia[2]	Canada[3]
1919		2,585	4,863	439	10,176
1920		882	2,739	635	4,866
1921		958	3,231	653	5,689
1922		405	2,284	562	3,976
1923		675	1,949	633	4,158
1924	774	802	1,936	654	4,230
1925	953	986	2,618	888	5,899
1926	665	1,689	3,904	1,233	7,893
1927	460	1,642	5,401	926	8,641
1928	294	1,096	4,343	656	6,606
1929	206	872	2,510	540	4,274
1930	160	589	1,544	681	3,282
1931	284	458	1,258	663	2,739
1932	289	411	1,203	562	2,530
1933	521	503	1,309	721	3,171
1934	682	627	1,495	763	3,728
1935	700	879	2,123	759	4,624
1936	443	1,816	2,052	668	5,237
1937	226	1,195	1,418	520	3,505
1938	214	1,194	1,353	590	3,399
1939	161	797	1,372	504	2,886
1940	148	528	853	621	2,212
1941	241	960	834	1,297	3,408
1942	317	609	659	406	2,165
1943	490	924	1,097	700	3,319
1944	418	792	1,213	759	3,662
1945	315	1,147	1,626	704	4,150
1946	24	1,155	1,795	946	4,189
1947	50	999	968	681	2,823
1948	11	1,160	1,435	564	4,407
1949	54	1,342	589	470	2,710
1950	261	1,413	798	911	3,707
1951	559	1,026	2,250	578	5,274
1952	463	1,100	2,559	744	5,533
1953	768	1,032	2,550	668	5,794
1954	1,189	1,219	3,281	664	6,790
1955	524	1,401	3,240	618	6,324
1956	338	1,342	2,368	459	5,076
1957	275	1,515	3,173		

[1] Obtained from E. F. Bossenmaier (*in litt.*), Game Branch, Manitoba Department of Mines and Natural Resources.

[2] Obtained from C. J. Ducharme (*in litt.*), Ontario Department of Lands and Forests, having been compiled from Dominion Bureau of Statistics data.

[3] Taken from the *Canada Yearbook*, issued annually by the Dominion Bureau of Statistics.

TABLE R
Numbers of hawks and owls destroyed by
British Columbia Division of Predator
Control[1]

Year	Hawks	Owls	Total
1948	580	243	823
1949	520	179	699
1950	386	186	572
1951	300	109	409
1952	364	165	529
1953	422	273	695
1954	497	309	806
1955	215	186	401
1956	215	121	336
1957	190	90	280
1958	121	126	247

[1] Obtained from G. A. West (*in litt.*), Division of Predator Control, Fish and Game Branch, British Columbia Department of Recreation and Conservation.

TABLE S
Numbers of goshawks and horned owls bountied in Pennsylvania[1]

Biological year	Goshawk	Horned owl	Biological year	Goshawk	Horned owl
1929	76		1944	23	643
1930	28		1945	118	1,291
1931	46		1946	70	1,464
1932	64		1947	22	1,429
1933	68		1948	23	1,836
1934	172		1949	44	1,942
1935	701		1950	32	1,477
1936	1,080		1951		1,714
1937	144	751	1952		1,688
1938	52	1,046	1953		1,237
1939	82	44	1954		1,233
1940	31		1955		1,091
1941	29		1956		1,234
1942	15		1957		1,115
1943	60		1958		1,047

[1] Obtained from M. J. Golden (*in litt.*), Pennsylvania Game Commission; bounties were not paid during years for which no figure is shown.

✦✦

Literature Cited

Index

Literature Cited

References marked with an asterisk (*) were used in compiling Fig. 14; those marked with a dagger (†) were used in compiling Fig. 22.

ADAMS, L. 1951. Confidence limits for the Petersen or Lincoln index used in animal population studies. J. Wildl. Mgmt., 15(1):13–19.
———. 1959. An analysis of a population of snowshoe hares in northwestern Montana. Ecol. Monographs, 29(2):141–70.
ADAMS, L., S. B. SALVIN, and W. J. HADLOW. 1956. Ringworm in a population of snowshoe hares. J. Mammal., 37(1):94–99.
AIRAKSINEN, K. 1946. Kanalintujen runsaudenvaihtelusta Suomessa. Suomen Riista, 1:75–92.
ALDOUS, C. M. 1937. Notes on the life history of the snowshoe hare. J. Mammal., 18(1):46–57.
ALLEN, A. A., and P. P. LEVINE. 1935. A brief study of the willow ptarmigan and its relation to predators and Leucocytozoon disease. Trans. Am. Game Conf., 21:381–86.
AMMANN, G. A. 1957. The prairie grouse of Michigan. Game Div., Mich. Dept. Cons., Lansing. 200 pp.
ANDERSEN, J. 1957. Studies in Danish hare-populations. Danish Rev. Game Biol., 3(2):85–131.
ANDERSON, P. K. 1961. Density, social structure, and nonsocial environment in house-mouse populations and the implications for regulation of numbers. Trans. N.Y. Acad. Sci., Ser. II, 23(5):447–51.
ANDERSON, R. M. 1928. The fluctuation in the population of wild mammals, and the relationship of this fluctuation to conservation. Can. Field-Nat., 42(8):189–91.
*———. 1937. Mammals and birds of the Western Arctic District, Northwest Territories, Canada. Canada's Western Northland, 1937, pp. 97–122.
*ANONYMOUS. 1915. Local observations. In Report of the Alberta Natural History Society. Alta. Dept. Agric. Ann. Rpt., pp. 291–92.

————. 1932. Report of the game commissioner. Alta. Dept. Agric. Ann. Rpt.

*————. 1935. The snowshoe rabbit or varying hare. Univ. Alaska Agric. Exp. Stn., Prog. Rpt. No. 5, pp. 18–19.

ATWOOD, E. L. 1956. Validity of mail survey data on bagged waterfowl. J. Wildl. Mgmt., 20(1):1–16.

†AUSTIN, O. L. 1932. The birds of Newfoundland Labrador. Mem. Nuttall Ornith. Club, No. 7. 229 pp.

*BAILEY, R. A. 1946. Reading rabbit population cycles from pines. Wisc. Cons. Bull., 11(7):14–17.

BAKER, F. S. 1950. Principles of silviculture. New York: McGraw-Hill. 414 pp.

*BANFIELD, F. A. [A. W. F.] 1941. Notes on Saskatchewan mammals. Can. Field-Nat., 55(8):117–23.

*BANFIELD, A. W. F. 1951. Notes on the mammals of the Mackenzie District, Northwest Territories. Arctic, 4(2):113–21.

*————. 1958. The mammals of Banff National Park, Alberta. Natl. Mus. Can. Bull. No. 159, Biol. Ser. No. 57. 53 pp.

BARICK, F. B., and T. S. CRITCHER. 1956. Statistical game kill surveys — some observations on five years of operation. Proc. S.E. Assoc. Game and Fish Commissioners Meeting, Dec. 1955, pp. 43–54.

BELLROSE, F. C. 1947. Analysis of methods used in determining game kill. J. Wildl. Mgmt., 11(2):105–19.

BOUGHTON, R. V. 1932. The influence of helminth parasitism on the abundance of the snowshoe rabbit in western Canada. Can. J. Res., 7(5):524–47.

————. 1937. Endoparasitic infestations in grouse, their pathogenicity and correlation with meteoro-topographical conditions. Univ. Minn. Agric. Exp. Stn. Tech. Bull. 121. 50 pp.

* BRADSHAW, F. 1922–23. Reports of the chief game guardian. Sask. Dept. Agric. Ann. Rpts.

*————. 1924–27. Reports of the game commissioner. Sask. Dept. Agric. Ann. Rpts.

BRAESTRUP, F. W. 1940. The periodic die-off in certain herbivorous mammals and birds. Science, 92(2390):354–55.

————. 1941. A study on the arctic fox in Greenland. Immigrations, fluctuations in numbers based mainly on trading statistics. Medd. om Grønland, 13(4):1–101.

BRANDT, H. 1943. Alaska bird trails. Cleveland: Bird Research Foundation. 464 pp.

BRASSARD, J. A., and R. BERNARD. 1937. Willow ptarmigan at the Quebec Zoological Gardens. Auk, 54(4):514–15.

BRONSON, F. H., and O. W. TIEMEIER. 1959. The relationship of precipitation and black-tailed jack rabbit populations in Kansas. Ecology, 40(2):194–98.

*BROOKS, M. 1955. An isolated population of the Virginia varying hare. J. Wildl. Mgmt., 19(1):54–61.

BROUN, M. 1948. Hawks aloft: the story of Hawk Mountain. New York: Dodd, Mead Co. 222 pp.

*BUCHANAN, A. 1920. Wild life in Canada. New York: Stokes. 264 pp.

*†BUCKLEY, J. L. 1954. Animal population fluctuations in Alaska — a history. Trans. N. Am. Wildl. Conf., 19:338–57.

BUMP, G. 1939. Some characteristics of the periodic fluctuations in abundance of ruffed grouse. Trans. N. Am. Wildl. Conf., 4:478–84.

BUMP, G., R. W. DARROW, F. C. EDMINSTER, and W. F. CRISSEY. 1947. The ruffed grouse. N.Y. State Cons. Dept. 915 pp.

BURNHAM, J. B. 1918. Why grouse are scarce. American Game, Jan. 1918, pp. 4–7.

BUSS, I. O. 1950. In discussion of Rowan (1950a) paper. Trans. N. Am. Wildl. Conf., 15:382.

BUSS, I. O., and H. E. BUSS. 1947. Deer hunting records from central Bayfield County, 1930–46. Wisc. Cons. Bull., 12(1):5–11.

BUTLER, L. 1942. Fur cycles and conservation. Trans. N. Am. Wildl. Conf., 7:463–72.

———. 1945. Distribution and genetics of the color phases of the red fox in Canada. Genetics, 30(1)39–50.

———. 1947. The genetics of the color phases of the red fox in the Mackenzie River locality. Can. J. Res., D25(5):190–215.

———. 1950. Canada's wild fur crop. The Beaver, Dec. 1950. 6 pp.

———. 1951. Population cycles and color phase genetics of the colored fox in Quebec. Can. J. Zool., 29(1):24–41.

———. 1953. The nature of cycles in populations of Canadian mammals. Can. J. Zool., 31(2):242–62.

*BUTLER, W. F. 1873. The wild northland. London: Sampson, Low, Marston, Low, and Searle. 358 pp.

CABOT, W. B. 1912. In northern Labrador. Boston: Barger. 292 pp.

†CADE, T. J., and J. L. BUCKLEY. 1953. A mass emigration of sharp-tailed grouse from the Tanana Valley, Alaska, in 1934. Condor, 55(6):313.

CAMERON, A. W. 1950. Arctic fox on Cape Breton Island. Can. Field-Nat., 64(4):154.

CARTWRIGHT, B. W. 1944. The "crash" decline in sharp-tailed grouse and Hungarian partridge in western Canada and the role of the predator. Trans. N. Am. Wildl. Conf., 9:324–30.

CHITTENDEN, H. M. 1954. The American fur trade of the far west. Vol. 1. Stanford: Academic Reprints. 482 pp.

CHITTY, D. 1952. Mortality among voles (*Microtus agrestis*) at Lake Vyrnwy, Montgomeryshire in 1936–9. Phil. Trans. Roy. Soc. Lon., *B638*(236):505–52.

———. 1955. Adverse effects of population density upon the viability of later generations. In The numbers of man and animals. Edinburgh: Oliver & Boyd Ltd. 152 pp.

———. 1957. Self-regulation of numbers through changes in viability. Cold Spring Harbor Symposia on Quant. Biol., *22*:277–80.

———. 1959. A note on shock disease. Ecology, *40*(4):728–31.

*CHITTY, D., and H. CHITTY. 1941. Canadian arctic wild life enquiry, 1939–40. J. An. Ecol., *10*(2):184–203.

———. 1942. The snowshoe rabbit enquiry, 1939–40. Can. Field-Nat., *55*(2):17–21.

CHITTY, D., and C. ELTON. 1937. The snowshoe rabbit enquiry 1935–36. Can. Field-Nat., *51*(5):63–73.

———. 1938. The snowshoe rabbit enquiry 1936–37. Can. Field-Nat., *52*(5):63–72.

———. 1939. The snowshoe rabbit enquiry 1937–38. Can. Field-Nat., *53*(5):63–71.

*———. 1940. The snowshoe rabbit enquiry 1938–39. Can. Field-Nat., *54*(8):117–24.

CHITTY, D., and M. NICHOLSON. 1943. The snowshoe rabbit enquiry, 1940–41. Can. Field-Nat., *57*(4, 5):64–68.

CHITTY, H. 1943. The snowshoe rabbit enquiry, 1941–42. Can. Field-Nat., *57*(7, 8):136–41.

———. 1946. The snowshoe rabbit enquiry, 1942–43. Can. Field-Nat., *60*(3):67–70.

———. 1948. The snowshoe rabbit enquiry, 1943–46. J. An. Ecol., *17*(1):39–44.

———. 1950. The snowshoe rabbit enquiry, 1946–48. J. An. Ecol., *19*(1):15–20.

CHRISTIAN, J. J. 1950. The adreno-pituitary system and population cycles in mammals. J. Mammal., *31*(3):247–59.

———. 1961. Phenomena associated with population density. Proc. Natl. Acad. Sci., *47*(4):428–49.

CLARK, S. H. 1933–36. Reports of the game commissioner. Alta. Dept. Agric. Ann. Rpts.

CLARKE, C. H. D. 1936. Fluctuations in numbers of ruffed grouse, *Bonasa umbellus* (Linné), with special reference to Ontario. Univ. Toronto Studies, Biol. Ser. No. 41. 118 pp.

———. 1942. Bernard Rogan Ross to Spencer Fullerton Baird. Can. Field-Nat., 56(8, 9):120–22.

———. 1944. Notes on the status and distribution of certain mammals and birds in the Mackenzie River and western Arctic area in 1942 and 1943. Can. Field-Nat., 58(3):97–103.

———. 1949. Fluctuations in populations. J. Mammal., 30(1):21–25.

CLOPPER, C. J., and E. S. PEARSON. 1934. The use of confidence or fiducial limits illustrated in the case of the binomial. Biometrika, 26:404-13.

COLE, L. C. 1951. Population cycles and random oscillations. J. Wildl. Mgmt., 15(3):233–52.

———. 1954. Some features of random population cycles. J. Wildl. Mgmt., 18(1):2–24.

———. 1956. Population fluctuations. Proc. 10th Int. Cong. Ent., 2:639–47.

———. 1957. Sketches of general and comparative demography. Cold Spring Harbor Symposia on Quant. Biol., 22:287–300.

COOK, D. B., and S. B. ROBESON. 1945. Varying hare and forest succession. Ecology, 26(4):406–10.

*COWAN, I. M. 1938. The fur trade and the fur cycle: 1825–1857. B.C. Hist. Quart., 2:19–30.

———. 1949. Rabies as a possible population control of arctic Canidae. J. Mammal., 30(4):396–98.

———. 1955. Birds of Jasper National Park, Alberta, Canada. Can. Wildl. Serv. Wildl. Mgmt. Bull., Ser. 2, No. 8. 66 pp.

COWAN, I. M., and R. H. MACKAY. 1950. Food habits of the marten (*Martes americana*) in the Rocky Mountain region of Canada. Can. Field-Nat., 64(3):100–104.

*COX, W. T. 1936. Snowshoe rabbit migration, tick infestation, and weather cycles. J. Mammal., 17(3):216–21.

CRIDDLE, N. 1930. Some natural factors governing the fluctuations of grouse in Manitoba. Can. Field-Nat., 44(4):77–80.

†CRIDDLE, S. 1935. Christmas bird censuses, 1934: Aweme, Manitoba. Can. Field-Nat., 49(2):44.

*———. 1938. A study of the snowshoe rabbit. Can. Field-Nat., 52(3):31–40.

*CRISSEY, W. F., and R. W. DARROW. 1949. A study of predator control on Valcour Island. N.Y. State Cons. Dept., Div. Fish and Game, Res. Ser. No. 1. 28 pp.

CRONAN, J. M. 1960. Prestige and memory bias in hunter kill surveys. R.I. Div. Game and Fish, Providence. 7 pp. Mimeo.

CROSS, E. C. 1940. Periodic fluctuations in numbers of the red fox in Ontario. J. Mammal., 21(3):294–306.

DANILOFF, D. N. 1953. Principles of typology and valuation of trapping areas. Can. Wildl. Serv., Translations Russ. Game Rpts., 6:84–133.

DAVIDSON, V. E. 1940. An 8-year census of lesser prairie chickens. J. Wildl. Mgmt., 4(1):55–62.

DAVIS, D. E. 1957. The existence of cycles. Ecology, 38(1):163–64.

DEANE, R. 1907. Unusual abundance of the American goshawk (*Accipiter atricapillus*). Auk., 24(2):182–86.

DEVANY, J. L. 1923. Arctic fox shot in Cape Breton. Can. Field-Nat., 37(6):118.

DE VOS, A., and S. E. MATEL. 1952. The status of the lynx in Canada, 1920–1952. J. Forest., 50(10):742–45.

DE VOS, A., A. T. CRINGAN, J. K. REYNOLDS, and H. G. LUMSDEN. 1959. Biological investigations of traplines in northern Ontario, 1951–56. Ont. Dept. Lands and Forests, Tech. Bull. Wildl. Ser. No. 8. 62 pp.

°DICE, L. R. 1921. Notes on the mammals of interior Alaska. J. Mammal., 2(1):20–28.

DOMINION BUREAU OF STATISTICS. The Canada year book. Issued annually by Dept. Trade and Comm., Ottawa.

DORNEY, R. S. 1959. Relation of hunting, weather and parasitic disease to Wisconsin ruffed grouse populations. Univ. Wisc., unpub. Ph.D. Thesis. 94 pp.

DORNEY, R. S., and C. KABAT. 1960. Relation of weather, parasitic disease and hunting to Wisconsin ruffed grouse populations. Wisc. Cons. Dept., Madison, Tech. Bull. No. 20. 64 pp.

DORNEY, R. S., D. R. THOMPSON, J. B. HALE, and R. F. WENDT. 1958. An evaluation of ruffed grouse drumming counts. J. Wildl. Mgmt., 22(1):35–40.

DYMOND, J. R. 1947. Fluctuations in animal populations with special reference to those of Canada. Trans. Roy. Soc. Can., 41(5)1–34.

EATON, W. F. 1934. Eighteen years of Wyanokie (1916–1933). Abst. Proc. Linn. Soc. N.Y., No. 43–44:14–26.

EDWARDS, R. Y., and I. M. COWAN. 1957. Fur production of the boreal forest of British Columbia. J. Wildl. Mgmt., 21(2):257–67.

†EKLAND, C. R. 1956. Bird and mammal notes from the interior Ungava Peninsula. Can. Field-Nat., 70(2):69–76.

ELSEY, C. A. 1954. A case of cannibalism in Canada lynx (*Lynx canadensis*). J. Mammal., 35(1):129.

ELTON, C. 1924. Periodic fluctuations in the numbers of animals: their causes and effects. Br. J. Exp. Biol., 2(1):119–63.

——. 1931. The study of epidemic diseases among wild animals. J. Hyg., 31(4):435–56.

———. 1933. The Canadian snowshoe rabbit enquiry, 1931–32. Can. Field-Nat., *47*(4):63–69, *47*(5):84–86.

———. 1934. The Canadian snowshoe rabbit enquiry, 1932–33. Can. Field-Nat., *48*(5):73–78.

———. 1942. Voles, mice and lemmings. Oxford: Clarendon Press. 496 pp.

ELTON, C., and M. NICHOLSON. 1942a. Fluctuations in numbers of the muskrat (*Ondatra zibethica*) in Canada. J. An. Ecol., *11*(1):96–126.

———. 1942b. The ten-year cycle in numbers of the lynx in Canada. J. An. Ecol., *11*(2):215–44.

ELTON, C., and G. SWYNNERTON. 1935. The Canadian snowshoe rabbit enquiry, 1933–34. Can. Field-Nat., *49*(5):79–85.

———. 1936. The Canadian snowshoe rabbit enquiry, 1934–35. Can. Field-Nat., *50*(5):71–81.

ERICKSON, A. B. 1938. Grouse observations. The Flicker, *10*(3, 4):14.

———. 1944. Helminth infections in relation to population fluctuations in snowshoe hares. J. Wildl. Mgmt., 8(2):134–53.

ERICKSON, A. B., and D. W. BURCALOW. 1953. Minnesota's game kill. The Conservation Volunteer, Minn. Cons. Dept., *16*(94):27–37.

ERICKSON, A. B., P. R. HIGHBY, and C. E. CARLSON. 1949. Ruffed grouse populations in Minnesota in relation to blood and intestinal parasitism. J. Wildl. Mgmt., *13*(2):188–94.

ERRINGTON, P. L. 1954. On the hazards of overemphasizing numerical fluctuations in studies of "cyclic" phenomena in muskrat populations. J. Wildl. Mgmt., *18*(1):66–90.

———. 1957. Of population cycles and unknowns. Cold Spring Harbor Symposia on Quant. Biol., *22*:287–300.

FALLIS, A. M. 1945. Population trends and blood parasites of ruffed grouse in Ontario. J. Wildl. Mgmt., 9(3):203–6.

FISHER, L. W. 1939. Studies of the eastern ruffed grouse (*Bonasa umbellus umbellus*) in Michigan. Mich. State Coll., Agric. Exp. Stn. Tech. Bull. No. 166, 46 pp.

FISHER, R. A., and F. YATES. 1948. Statistical tables for biological, agricultural and medical research. London: Oliver & Boyd. 112 pp.

FLEMING, J. H. 1907. Birds of Toronto, Canada. Auk., *24*(1):71–89.

FORBUSH, E. H. 1927. Birds of Massachusetts and other New England States. Pt. 2. Mass. Dept. Agric. 461 pp.

FORMOZOV, A. N. 1942. Study of fluctuations in the numbers of exploited animals and the organization of "yield forecasts" in game management in the U.S.S.R. between 1917 and 1942. (Russian.) Translation by J. D. Jackson for Bur. An. Pop., Oxford Univ., England.

†FOWLE, C. D. 1960. A study of the blue grouse (*Dendragapus obscurus* (Say)) on Vancouver Island, British Columbia. Can. J. Zool., 38(4):701–13.

FRANK, F. 1957. The causality of microtine cycles in Germany. J. Wildl. Mgmt., 21(2):113–21.

GAUSE, G. F. 1934. The struggle for existence. Baltimore: Williams & Wilkins. 163 pp.

GORDON, S. 1940. An analysis of methods used to collect game kill statistics. Penn. Game News, 11(8):22–23, 30–31.

GOWAN, E. H. 1948. Solar ultra-violet at Edmonton. J. Roy. Astro. Soc. Can., 42:161–65.

GRABER, R. R., and J. S. GOLDEN. 1960. Hawks and owls: population trends from Illinois Christmas counts. Ill. Nat. Hist. Surv., Biol. Notes No. 41. 24 pp.

GRAHAM, S. A., and G. S. HUNT. 1958. A noncyclic ruffed grouse population near Ann Arbor, Michigan. J. Wildl. Mgmt., 22(4)427–32.

*GRANGE, W. B. 1932. Observations on the snowshoe hare, *Lepus americanus phaeonotus* Allen. J. Mammal., 13(1):1–19.

*———. 1936. Some observations on the ruffed grouse in Wisconsin. Wils. Bull., 48(2):104–10.

———. 1949. The way to game abundance. New York: Scribner's. 365 pp.

———. [1950]. Wisconsin grouse problems. Wisc. Cons. Dept., Madison, 318 pp.

GREEN, R. G., and C. A. EVANS. 1940. Studies on a population cycle of snowshoe hares on the Lake Alexander area. J. Wildl. Mgmt., 4(2):220–38, 4(3):267–78, 4(4):247–58.

GREEN, R. G., and C. L. LARSON. 1938. A description of shock disease in the snowshoe hare. Am. J. Hyg., 28(2):190–212.

GREEN, R. G., and J. E. SCHILLINGER. 1935. Progress report of wildlife disease studies for 1934. Trans. Am. Game Conf., 21:397–401.

GREEN, R. G., C. A. EVANS, and C. L. LARSON. 1943. A ten-year population study of the rabbit tick *Haemaphysalis leporis-palustris*. Am. J. Hyg., 38:260–81.

GREEN, R. G., C. L. LARSON, and J. F. BELL. 1939. Shock disease as the cause of the periodic decimation of the snowshoe hare. Am. J. Hyg., 30B(3):83–102.

GREEN, R. G., C. L. LARSON, and D. W. MATHER. 1938. The natural occurrence of shock disease in hares. Trans. N. Am. Wildl. Conf., 3:877–81.

GRINNELL, J. 1917. An invasion of California by the eastern Goshawk. Condor, 19(2):70–71.

GROSS, A. O. 1928. The heath hen. Mem. Boston Soc. Nat. Hist., 6(4):491–588.

———. 1930. Progress report of the Wisconsin prairie chicken investigation. Wisc. Cons. Comm., Madison. 112 pp.

———. 1947. Cyclic invasions of the snowy owl and the migration of 1945–1946. Auk, 64(4):584–601.

GUDMUNDSSON, F. 1958. Some reflections on ptarmigan cycles. Paper given at 12th Int. Ornith. Cong., Helsinki, June 1958. 10 pp. Mimeo.

GULLION, G. W. 1954. Western states sage grouse questionnaire. No. 1. 14 pp. Mimeo.

*GUNN, D. 1867. Notes on an egging expedition to Shoal Lake, west of Lake Winnipeg. Smith. Inst. Rpt. 1867, pp. 427–32.

HAMERSTROM, F. N. 1939. A study of Wisconsin prairie chicken and sharp-tailed grouse. Wils. Bull., 51(2):105–20.

HAMERSTROM, F. N., and F. HAMERSTROM. 1951. Mobility of the sharp-tailed grouse in relation to its ecology and distribution. Am. Mid. Nat., 46(1):174–226.

———. 1955. Population density and behavior in Wisconsin prairie chickens (*Tympanuchus cupido pinnatus*). Int. Ornith. Cong., 11:459–66.

HANSON, H. C. 1953. Muskeg as sharp-tailed grouse habitat. Wils. Bull., 65(4):235–41.

*HARPER, F. 1932. Mammals of the Athabaska and Great Slave Lakes region. J. Mammal., 13(1):19–36.

HARRISON, A. H. 1908. In search of a polar continent. London: Edward Arnold. 292 pp.

*HAWORTH, P. L. 1917. On the headwaters of Peace River. New York: Scribner's. 295 pp.

HAYNE, D. W. 1949. An examination of the strip census method for estimating animal populations. J. Wildl. Mgmt., 13(2):145–57.

*HENDERSON, A. D. 1923. Cycles of abundance and scarcity in certain mammals and birds. J. Mammal., 4(4):264–65.

HESS, Q. F. 1946. A trapper's record of animal abundance in the Oba-Hearst area of Ontario for the years 1931–1944. Can. Field-Nat., 60(2):31–33.

HEWITT, C. G. 1921. The conservation of the wild life of Canada. New York: Scribner's. 344 pp.

HICKEY, J. J. 1954. Mean intervals in indices of wildlife populations. J. Wildl. Mgmt., 18(1):90–106.

———. 1955. Some American population research on gallinaceous birds. In Recent Studies in Avian Biology. Urbana: Univ. Ill. Press. 479 pp.

*HIND, H. Y. 1860. Narrative of the Canadian Red River expedition of 1857 and of the Assinniboine and Saskatchewan exploring expedition of 1858. 2 Vol., London: Longman, Green, Longman, and Roberts. 494 pp. and 472 pp.

HOFFMANN, R. S. 1956. Observations on a sooty grouse population at Sage Hen Creek, California. Condor, 58(5):321–37.

———. 1958. The role of predators in "cyclic" declines of grouse populations. J. Wildl. Mgmt., 22(3):317–19.

HOUSTON, C. S. 1949. The birds of the Yorkton district, Saskatchewan. Can. Field-Nat., 63(6):215–41.

†HOUSTON, C. S., and M. G. STREET. 1959. The birds of the Saskatchewan River Carlton to Cumberland. Sask. Nat. Hist. Soc. Spec. Pub. No. 2. 205 pp.

HOWELL, A. B. 1923. Periodic fluctuations in the numbers of small mammals. J. Mammal., 4(3):149–55.

HUNGERFORD, K. E. 1951. Ruffed grouse populations and cover use in northern Idaho. Trans. N. Am. Wildl. Conf., 16:216–24.

HUNTINGTON, E. 1945. Mainsprings of civilization. New York: John Wiley & Sons. 660 pp.

HUTCHINSON, G. E. 1942. Nati sunt mures, et facta est confusio. Review of Voles, Mice and Lemmings (Elton, 1942). Quart. Rev. Biol., 17(4):354–57.

HUTCHINSON, G. E., and E. S. DEEVEY. 1949. Ecological studies on populations. In Survey of Biological Progress. New York: Academic Press Inc. 396 pp.

INNIS, H. A. 1927. The fur-trade of Canada. Toronto: Oxford University Press. 172 pp.

*JOHNSON, C. E. 1930. Recollections of the mammals of northwestern Minnesota. J. Mammal., 11(4):435–52.

JOHNSON, M. D. 1958. Ruffed grouse roadside drumming survey. N. Dak. P-R Rpt., Proj. W-35-R-5, May 1958. 2 pp. Mimeo.

KEITH, L. B. 1959. Some sex and age ratios among Hungarian partridges and sharp-tailed grouse. Trans. Organiz. Mtg. Can. Soc. Wildl. and Fish. Biologists, Ottawa, Jan. 1958. 14 pp. Mimeo.

———. 1960. Observations on snowy owls at Delta, Manitoba. Can. Field-Nat., 74(2):106–12.

*KINDLE, E. M. 1928. Canada north of fifty-six degrees. Can. Field-Nat., 42(3):53–86.

KING, R. T. 1937. Ruffed grouse management. J. Forest., 35(6):523–32.

KIRIS, I. D. 1953. On the theory of population numbers of economic wild animals and forecasting their "crops." Can. Wildl. Serv., Translations Russ. Game Rpts., 6:1–53.

KLOSTER, R. 1921. Veksling i rypebestanden Norsk opfatning. Norsk Jaeg. og FiskForen. Tidsskr., *50*:317–32.

KOSKIMIES, J. 1955. Ultimate causes of cyclic fluctuations in numbers in animal population. Finnish Game Foundation, Papers on Game Research No. 15. 29 pp.

KRUMHOLZ, L. A., R. W. DARROW, O. H. HEWITT, and E. L. KOZICKY. 1957. Glossary of wildlife terms. J. Wildl. Mgmt., *21*(3):373–76.

LACK, D. 1954a. Cyclic mortality. J. Wildl. Mgmt., *18*(1):25–37.

———. 1954b. The natural regulation of animal numbers. Oxford: Clarendon Press. 343 pp.

°LAING, H. M., P. A. TAVERNER, and R. M. ANDERSON. 1929. Birds and mammals of the Mount Logan expedition, 1925. Natl. Mus. Can. Bull., *56*:69–107.

LAUCKHART, J. B. 1957. Animal cycles and food. J. Wildl. Mgmt., *21*(2):230–34.

°†LAWTON, B. 1907–31. Reports of the chief game guardian; Reports of the chief game and fire guardian; Reports of the game commissioner. Alta. Dept. Agric. Ann. Rpts.

LAYNE, J. N., and W. H. McKEON. 1956. Some aspects of red fox and gray fox reproduction in New York. N. Y. Fish and Game J., *3*(1):44–74.

LENSINK, C. J., R. O. SKOOG, and J. L. BUCKLEY. 1955. Food habits of marten in interior Alaska and their significance. J. Wildl. Mgmt., *19*(3):364–68.

LEOPOLD, A. 1931. Report on a game survey of the North Central States. Madison: Sporting Arms and Ammunition Manufacturers Inst. 299 pp.

———. 1933. Game management. New York: Scribner's. 481 pp.

LEOPOLD, A., and J. N. BALL. 1931. British and American grouse cycles. Can. Field-Nat., *45*(7):162–67.

°LLOYD, H. 1936. The late Norman Criddle's record of the snowshoe rabbit (*Lepus americanus*) at Aweme, Manitoba. Can. Field-Nat., *50*(8):129–30.

McCABE, R. A., and A. S. HAWKINS. 1946. The Hungarian partridge of Wisconsin. Am. Mid. Nat., *36*(1):1–75.

†McDONALD, D. 1935. Some notes on the habits of the ruffed grouse, *Bonasa umbellus*. Can. Field-Nat., *49*(7):118.

°MacFARLANE, R. 1890. On an expedition down the Begh-ula or Anderson River. Can. Rec. Sci., *4*:28–53.

———. 1905. Notes on mammals collected and observed in the northern Mackenzie River District, Northwest Territories of Canada, with remarks on explorers and explorations of the far north. Proc. U.S. Natl. Mus., 28(1405):673–764.

MACKENZIE, J. M. D. 1952. Fluctuations in the numbers of British tetraonids. J. An. Ecol., 21(1):128–53.

*MacLULICH, D. A. 1937. Fluctuations in the numbers of the varying hare (*Lepus americanus*). Univ. Toronto Studies, Biol. Ser. No. 43. 136 pp.

———. 1957. The place of chance in population processes. J. Wildl. Mgmt., 21(3):293–99.

*MACOUN, J. 1882. Manitoba and the great North-west. Guelph: World Publishing Co. 687 pp.

MACOUN, J., and J. M. MACOUN. 1909. Catalogue of Canadian birds. Can. Dept. Mines, Geol. Surv. Branch Pub. 973. 761 pp.

*MAIR, C., and R. MACFARLANE. 1908. Through the Mackenzie Basin. Toronto: William Briggs. 494 pp.

*MANVILLE, R. H. 1948. The vertebrate fauna of the Huron Mountains, Michigan. Am. Mid. Nat., 39(3):615–40.

MARSH, D. B. 1938. The influx of the red fox and its color phases into the barren lands. Can. Field-Nat., 52(4):60–61.

MARSHALL, W. H. 1954. Ruffed grouse and snowshoe hare populations on the Cloquet Experimental Forest, Minnesota. J. Wildl. Mgmt., 18(1):109–12.

MATHESON, C. 1953. The partridge in Wales: a survey of gamebook records. Brit. Birds, 46(2):57–64.

———. 1956. Fluctuations in partridge populations. Brit. Birds, 49(3):112–14.

MIDDLETON, A. D. 1934. Periodic fluctuations in British game populations. J. An. Ecol., 3(2):231–49.

MILLER, W. L. 1959. Rural letter carrier roadside counts 1958–1959. N. Dak. P-R Rpt., Proj. W-35-R-6, June 1959.

MOHR, W. P., and C. O. MOHR. 1936. Recent jackrabbit populations at Rapidan, Minnesota. J. Mammal., 17(2):112–14.

MORAN, P. A. P. 1949. The statistical analysis of the sunspot and lynx cycles. J. An. Ecol., 18(1):115–16.

———. 1952. The statistical analysis of game-bird records. J. An. Ecol., 21(1):154–58.

———. 1953. The statistical analysis of the Canadian lynx cycle. Aust. J. Zool., 1(2):163–73, 1(3):291–98.

———. 1954. The logic of the mathematical theory of animal populations. J. Wildl. Mgmt., 18(1):60–66.

MORSE, M. 1939. A local study of predation upon hares and grouse during the cyclic decimation. J. Wildl. Mgmt., 3(3):203–11.

MOWAT, F. M. 1947. Notes on the birds of Emma Lake, Saskatchewan. Can. Field-Nat., 61(3):105–15.

*MUNRO, J. A. 1923. Winter bird life at Okanagan Landing, British Columbia, 1917 and 1918. Can. Field-Nat., 37(4):70–74.

†MURIE, A. 1946. Observations on the birds of Mount McKinley National Park, Alaska. Condor, 48(6):253–61.

MUSSELMAN, T. E. 1923. Bird banding at Thomasville, Ga., 1923. Auk, 40(3):442–52.

NEGUS, N. C., E. GOULD, and R. K. CHIPMAN. 1961. Ecology of the rice rat, *Oryzomys palustris* (Harlan), on Breton Island, Gulf of Mexico, with a critique of the social stress theory. Tulane Studies in Zool., 8(4):94–123.

*NELSON, E. W. 1909. The rabbits of North America. N. Am. Fauna No. 29. 314 pp.

OSGOOD, W. H. 1909. Biological investigations in Alaska and Yukon Territory. N. Am. Fauna No. 30. 96 pp.

PALMER, W. L. 1956. Ruffed grouse population studies on hunted and unhunted areas. Trans. N. Am. Wildl. Conf., 21:338–45.

PALMER, W. L., and L. EBERHARDT. 1955. Evaluation of the strip census method for ruffed grouse. Paper given at 17th Midwest Wildl. Conf. 5 pp. Mimeo.

PALMGREN, P. 1949. Some remarks on the short-term fluctuations in the numbers of northern birds and mammals. Oikos, 1(1):114–21.

PATTERSON, R. L. 1952. The sage grouse in Wyoming. Wyo. Game and Fish Comm. 341 pp.

*PEGG, F. H. 1928. Canadian Christmas bird census, 1927: Glenevis, Alberta. Can. Field-Nat., 42(4):101.

†PETERS, H. S., and T. D. BURLEIGH. 1951. The birds of Newfoundland. Nfld. Dept. Natural Resources, St. John's. 431 pp.

PETRABORG, W. H., E. G. WELLEIN, and V. E. GUNVALSON. 1953. Roadside drumming counts a spring census method for ruffed grouse. J. Wildl. Mgmt., 17(3):292–95.

*PHILIP, C. B. 1939. A parasitological reconnaissance in Alaska with particular reference to varying hares. J. Mammal., 20(1):82–86.

PHILLIPS, J. C. 1926. An investigation of the periodic fluctuations in the numbers of the ruffed grouse. Science, 63(1621):92–93.

———. 1937. Man's influence on ruffed grouse populations. Cambridge: Cosmos Press. Private Printing. 24 pp.

PITELKA, F. A. 1957. Some aspects of population structure in the short-term cycle of the brown lemming in northern Alaska. Cold Spring Harbor Symposia on Quant. Biol., 22:237–51.

PITELKA, F. A., P. Q. TOMICH, and G. W. TREICHEL. 1955. Breeding behavior of jaegers and owls near Barrow, Alaska. Condor, 57(1):3–18.

POLAND, H. 1892. Fur-bearing animals. London: Gurney & Jackson. 392 pp.

*PORSILD, A. E. 1945. Mammals of the Mackenzie Delta. Can. Field-Nat., 59(1):4–22.

*PREBLE, E. A. 1908. A biological investigation of the Athabaska-Mackenzie region. N. Am. Fauna No. 27. 574 pp.

RAND, A. L. 1948a. Mammals of the eastern Rockies and western plains of Canada. Natl. Mus. Can. Bull. No. 108, Biol. Series No. 35. 237 pp.

*———. 1948b. Mr. W. H. Bryenton's notes on Manitoba mammals of the Herb Lake-Flin Flon area. Can. Field-Nat., 62(5):140–50.

*RAUSCH, R. 1951. Notes on the Nunamiut Eskimo and mammals of the Anaktuvuk Pass region, Brooks Range, Alaska. Arctic, 4(3):147–95.

RICH, E. E., and A. M. JOHNSON. 1951. Cumberland House Journals and Inland Journals. First Series — 1775–79. London: Hudson's Bay Record Society. 382 pp.

———. 1952. Cumberland House Journals and Inland Journals. Second Series — 1779–82. London: Hudson's Bay Record Society. 313 pp.

———. 1954. Moose Fort Journals: 1783–85. London: Hudson's Bay Record Society. 392 pp.

*———. 1956. Eden Colvile's letters: 1849–52. London: Hudson's Bay Record Society. 300 pp.

RICHARDS, S. H., and R. L. HINE. 1953. Wisconsin fox populations. Wisc. Cons. Dept., Madison, Tech. Wildl. Bull. No. 6. 78 pp.

RICHARDSON, J. 1829. The quadrupeds. Pt. 1. Fauna Boreali-Americana. London: John Murray. 300 pp.

*RICHMOND, N. D., and H. R. ROSLAND. 1949. Mammal survey of northwestern Pennsylvania. Penn. Game Comm. and U.S. Fish and Wildl. Serv. 67 pp.

RICKER, W. E. 1948. Methods of estimating vital statistics of fish populations. Ind. Univ. Pub., Sci. Ser. No. 15. 101 pp.

ROBINSON, M. J., and J. L. ROBINSON. 1946. Fur production in the Northwest Territories. Can. Geographical J., Jan. 1946, pp. 2–16.

ROGERS, F. J. 1937. A preliminary list of the birds of Hillside Beach, Lake Winnipeg, Manitoba. Can. Field-Nat., 51(6):79–86.

*ROWAN, W. 1948. The ten-year cycle. Univ. Alta. Dept. Ext. 12 pp.

———. 1950a. The coming peak of the ten-year cycle in Canada. Trans. N. Am. Wildl. Conf., 15:379–83.

*———. 1950b. Canada's premier problem of animal conservation. New Biology, 9:38–57.

———. 1953. Hunters can aid research into game bird population changes. Within Our Borders [Prov. of Alta., Edmonton], 6:2.

———. 1954. Reflections on the biology of animal cycles. J. Wildl. Mgmt., 18(1):52–60.

ROWAN, W., and L. B. KEITH. 1956. Reproductive potential and sex ratios of snowshoe hares in northern Alberta. Can. J. Zool., 34(4):273–81.

RUDEN, I. 1927–40. Viltbestanden i (1926–39), Grafisk fremstillet. Norsk Jaeg. og FiskForen. Tidsskr., 56–69.

*RUSSEL, F. 1898. Explorations in the far north. Iowa City: Univ. Iowa. 290 pp.

*SANSON, E. N. 1913. Some notes on a winter's tramp up Sulphur Mountain, Banff. In Seventh Annual Report of the Alberta History Society. Alta. Dept. Agric. Ann. Rpt., pp. 226–28.

SCHMIDT, F. J. W. 1936. Winter food of the sharp-tailed grouse and pinnated grouse in Wisconsin. Wils. Bull. 48(3):181–203.

SCHORGER, A. W. 1944. The prairie chicken and sharp-tailed grouse in early Wisconsin. Trans. Wisc. Acad. Sci., Arts and Letters, 35:1–59.

———. 1945. The ruffed grouse in early Wisconsin. Trans. Wisc. Acad. Sci., Arts and Letters, 37:35–90.

SCHWARTZ, C. W. 1945. The ecology of the prairie chicken in Missouri. Univ. Mo. Studies, 20(1):1–99.

SETON, E. T. 1909. Life histories of northern animals. Vol. 1. New York: Scribner's. 673 pp.

———. 1911. The arctic prairies. New York: International University Press. 308 pp.

*———. 1929. Lives of game animals. New York: Doubleday, Doran & Co.

*SEVERAID, J. H. 1942. The snowshoe hare its life history and artificial propagation. Maine Dept. Inland Fish. and Game, Augusta. 95 pp.

*SHELDON, C. 1911. The wilderness of the upper Yukon. New York: Scribner's. 354 pp.

———. 1930. The wilderness of Denali. New York: Scribner's. 412 pp.

SHELFORD, V. E. 1943. The abundance of the collared lemming (*Dicrostonyx groenlandicus* (Tr.) var. *richardsoni* Mer.) in the Churchill area, 1929 to 1940. Ecology, 24(4):472–84.

———. 1951. Fluctuation of non-forest animal populations in the upper Mississippi basin. Ecol. Monographs, 21(2):149–81.

———. 1952. Paired factors and master factors in environmental relations. Ill. Acad. Sci. Trans., 45:155–60.

SHELFORD, V. E., and R. E. YEATTER. 1955. Some suggested relations of prairie chicken abundance to physical factors, especially rainfall and solar radiation. J. Wildl. Mgmt., *19*(2):233–42.

SHEPARD, E. E. 1937. A partridge conservation measure of 1721 in Quebec Province. Hunting and Fishing in Canada, 3(9):20.

SIIVONEN, L. 1948. Structure of short-cyclic fluctuations in numbers of mammals and birds in the northern parts of the northern hemisphere. Finnish Foundation for Game Preservation, Papers on Game Research No. 1. 166 pp.

———. 1952. On the reflection of short-term fluctuations in numbers in the reproduction of tetranoids. Finnish Game Foundation, Papers on Game Research No. 9. 43 pp.

———. 1954a. Some essential features of short-term population fluctuations. J. Wildl. Mgmt., *18*(1):38–45.

———. 1954b. On the short-term fluctuations in numbers of tetraonids. Finnish Game Foundation, Papers on Game Research No. 13. 10 pp.

———. 1956. The correlation between the fluctuations of partridge and European hare populations and the climatic conditions of winters in southwest Finland during the last thirty years. Finnish Game Foundation, Papers on Game Research No. 17. 30 pp.

———. 1957. The problem of the short-term fluctuations in numbers of tetraonids in Europe. Finnish Game Foundation, Papers on Game Research No. 19. 44 pp.

SIIVONEN, L., and J. KOSKIMIES. 1955. Population fluctuations and the lunar cycle. Finnish Game Foundation, Papers on Game Research No. 14. 22 pp.

SMITH, D. A., and J. B. FOSTER. 1957. Notes on the small mammals of Churchill, Manitoba. J. Mammal., *38*(1):98–115.

SMITH, R. H. 1950. Cottontail rabbit investigations. N.Y. State Cons. Dept., Div. Fish and Game, P-R Proj. 1-R, Supplement B. 84 pp.

*SMITH, R. W. 1940. The land mammals of Nova Scotia. Am. Mid. Nat., *24*(1):213–41.

SNYDER, L. L. 1935. A study of the sharp-tailed grouse. Univ. Toronto Studies, Biol. Ser. No. 40. 66 pp.

SNYDER, L. L., and T. M. SHORTT. 1936. A summary of data relative to a recent invasion of willow ptarmigan. Roy. Ont. Mus. Zool., Occasional Papers No. 3. 4 pp.

SOLOMON, M. E. 1949. The natural control of animal populations. J. An. Ecol., *18*(1):1–35.

SONDRINI, W. J. 1950. Estimating game from licensee reports. Conn. State Board of Fish. and Game, Hartford. 50 pp.

*SOPER, J. D. 1921. Notes on the snowshoe rabbit. J. Mammal., *2*(2):101–8.

*———. 1942. Mammals of Wood Buffalo Park, northern Alberta and District of Mackenzie. J. Mammal., 23(2):119–45.

*———. 1947. Observations on mammals and birds in the Rocky Mountains of Alberta. Can. Field-Nat., 61(5):143–73.

*———. 1948. Mammal notes from the Grand Prairie-Peace River region, Alberta. J. Mammal., 29(1):49–64.

*———. 1951a. The mammals of Elk Island National Park, Alberta, Canada. Can. Wildl. Serv. Wildl. Mgmt. Bull., Ser. 1, No. 3. 24 pp.

*———. 1951b. The mammals of Prince Albert National Park, Saskatchewan, Canada. Can. Wildl. Serv. Wildl. Mgmt. Bull., Ser. 1, No. 5. 48 pp.

*———. 1952a. The mammals of Riding Mountain National Park, Manitoba, Canada. Can. Wildl. Serv. Wildl. Mgmt. Bull., Ser. 1, No. 7. 34 pp.

†———. 1952b. The birds of Prince Albert National Park, Saskatchewan. Can. Wildl. Serv. Wildl. Mgmt. Bull., Ser. 2, No. 4. 83 pp.

†———. 1953. The birds of Riding Mountain National Park, Manitoba, Canada. Can. Wildl. Serv. Wildl. Mgmt. Bull., Ser. 2, No. 6. 54 pp.

SPIERS, J. M. 1939. Fluctuations in numbers of birds in the Toronto region. Auk., 56(4):411–19.

*STRONG, W. D. 1930. Notes on mammals of the Labrador interior. J. Mammal., 11(1):1–10.

*SURBER, T. 1932. The mammals of Minnesota. Minn. Dept. Cons., St. Paul. 84 pp.

SWANSON, C. V., and C. F. YOCOM. 1958. Upland game-bird populations in relation to cover and agriculture in southeastern Washington. Trans. N. Am. Wildl. Conf., 23:277–90.

SWARTH, H. S. 1936a. A list of birds of the Atlin region, British Columbia. Proc. Cal. Acad. Sci., Ser. 4, 23(2):35–58.

*———. 1936b. Mammals of the Atlin region, northwestern British Columbia. J. Mammal., 17(4):398–405.

TAVERNER, P. A. 1928. Birds of western Canada. Natl. Mus. Can. Bull. No. 41, Biol. Ser. No. 10. 379 pp.

*———. 1929. Random notes on the fluctuation in numbers of rodents and grouse in Canada. Can. Field-Nat., 43(7):162–64.

THOMPSON, D. Q. 1955. The role of food and cover in population fluctuations of the brown lemming at Point Barrow, Alaska. Trans. N. Am. Wildl. Conf., 20:166–76.

THOMPSON, D. R., C. W. LEMKE, and J. B. HALE. 1959. A preliminary proposal for revision of game and fur harvest estimates. Wisc. Cons. Dept., Madison. 5 pp. Mimeo.

THOMPSON, W. R. 1957. Influence of prenatal maternal anxiety on emotionality in young rats. Science, 125(3250):698–99.

†TOWNSEND, C. W., and G. M. ALLEN. 1907. Birds of Labrador. Proc. Boston Soc. Nat. Hist., 33(7):277–428.

†TUBBS, F. F. 1940. Grouse cycles. Michigan Conservation, 9(12):1, 10.

TUFTS, R. W. 1925. Notes on grouse and woodcock conditions in Nova Scotia, spring, 1923. Can. Field-Nat., 39(5):115–16.

TWITCHELL, A. H. 1921. Notes on the mammals of the lower Yukon region. J. Mammal., 2(1):40–41.

WATSON, A. 1956. Ecological notes on the lemmings *Lemmus trimucronatus* and *Dicrostonyx groenlandicus* in Baffin Island. J. An. Ecol., 25(3):289–302.

WESTERSKOV, K. 1943. Urfuglen. Copenhagen.

——. 1956. Productivity of New Zealand pheasant populations. N.Z. Dept. Intern. Affairs, Wildl. Pub. No. 40B. 144 pp.

*WHITNEY, C. 1896. On snowshoes to the Barren Grounds. New York: Harpers. 324 pp.

†WILLIAMS, G. R. 1954. Population fluctuations in some northern hemisphere game birds (Tetraonidae). J. An. Ecol., 23(1):1–34.

*WILLIAMS, M. Y. 1920. Notes on the fauna of the Moose River and the Mattagami and Abitibi tributaries. Can. Field-Nat., 34(10)121–26.

*——. 1921. Notes on the fauna of the lower Pagwachuan, lower Kenogami and lower Albany Rivers in Ontario. Can. Field-Nat., 35(5):94–98.

WILSON, E. A., and A. S. LESLIE. 1911. Grouse disease. In The Grouse in Health and Disease. Lovat, ed. London: Smith, Elder & Co. 512 pp.

WING, L. W. 1960. Scattered reports and latitudinal passage in rabbit and rodent cycles. J. Cycle Res., 9(2):51–66.

WISCONSIN CONSERVATION DEPARTMENT. 1931–59. Wisconsin game census reports; Wisconsin game kill charts; Wisconsin game kill and license sales charts. Game Mgmt. Div., Madison.

WODZICKI, K., and H. S. ROBERTS. 1960. Influence of population density on the adrenal and body weights of the wild rabbit *Oryctolagus cuniculus* L. in New Zealand. N.Z. J. Sci., 3(1):103–20.

YEATTER, R. E. 1943. The prairie chicken in Illinois. Ill. Nat. Hist. Surv., 22(4):377–416.

YOUNG, H. 1958. Some repeat data on the cardinal. Bird Banding, 29(4):219–23.

YOUNG, H., J. NEESS, and J. T. EMLEN. 1952. Heterogeneity of trap response in a population of house mice. J. Wildl. Mgmt., 16(2):169–80.

Index